MW00609626

You don't have to be
Vegan
to Enjoy these Meals
Healthy Eating, Healthy Bodies,
Through Healthy Scrumptious Foods
Carol Fitzgerald

Carol Fitzgerald

Cover photograph by Keri Fitzgerald Johnson
Various other photographs throughout by Mary Carol Fitzgerald

Today more than 4000 medical doctors confirm that a vegan diet is more than adequate to promote and maintain good health. Further, if everyone gifted themselves with at least three months of a vegetarian diet, they would experience such a remarkable difference in their digestion, mental acuity and energy levels that they would want to continue.

—Viktoras Kulvinskas

Nutritionist, visionary author of the inspirational Survival into the 21st Century, Practitioner in the holistic field for more than 35 years, the "Father of Living Foods" and co-founder of the Hippocrates Health Institute.

Embracing Beautiful Moments

Portrait of a Child

Once Upon A Taste Feast

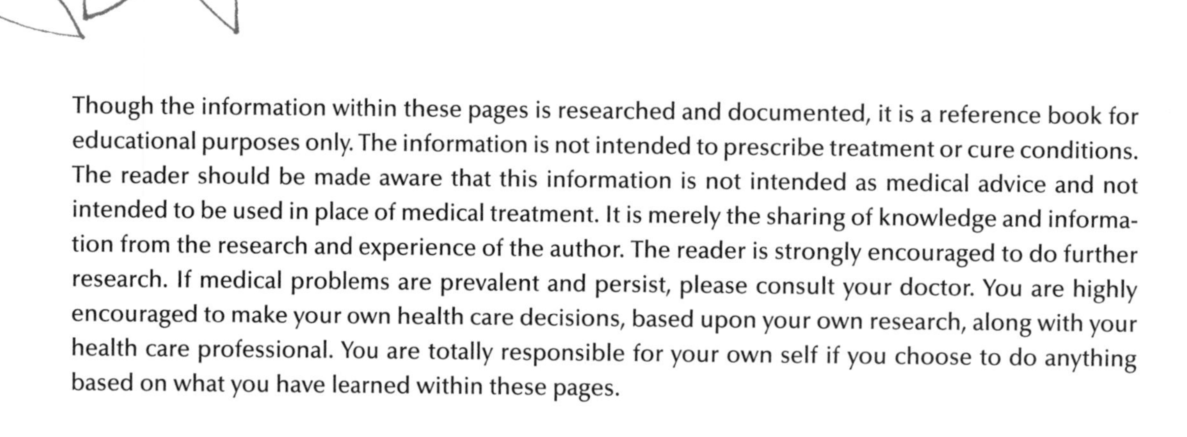

Though the information within these pages is researched and documented, it is a reference book for educational purposes only. The information is not intended to prescribe treatment or cure conditions. The reader should be made aware that this information is not intended as medical advice and not intended to be used in place of medical treatment. It is merely the sharing of knowledge and information from the research and experience of the author. The reader is strongly encouraged to do further research. If medical problems are prevalent and persist, please consult your doctor. You are highly encouraged to make your own health care decisions, based upon your own research, along with your health care professional. You are totally responsible for your own self if you choose to do anything based on what you have learned within these pages.

You Don't Have to be Vegan to Enjoy These Meals:
Healthy Eating , Healthy Bodies Through Healthy Scrumptious Foods
Carol Fitzgerald

The Carobi Five Publishing Group
Naples, Florida

Library of Congress Control Number: 2009912411
Fitzgerald, Carol

ISBN 0-9641596-6-X

Printed in the United States of America

www.Carobi5.com

For All Those Everywhere Who Desire Better Health

Especially

Bill

Patrick

Keri, Kennedy and Kerigan

Daniel

William, Sabrina, Will and Marlaina

Mary Carol

And For All Those Who Aren't There Yet

A Keepsake Book with Matters of the Heart Home and Health

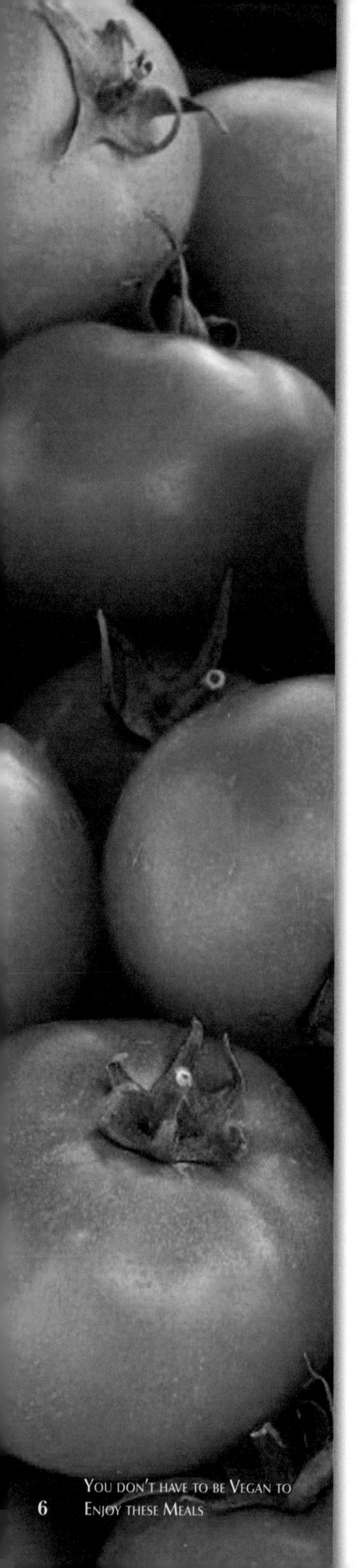

Table of Contents

Part One

Health and Wellness

Introduction 12
Why Vegan? 13
Genetics 16
What You Think and How it Affects You 17
Change is Not Easy 18
Vegan vs. Vegetarian 19
Protein 19
Combining Foods 21
Mercury 21
Organic versus Conventional Foods 22
Weight Loss 24
People ask me all the time, "What do you Eat?" 25
Sugar and Artificial Sweeteners 26
What CAN We Use As a Sweetener 29
Fats 30
Good Carbs versus Bad Carbs 31
Osteoporosis/Calcium/Dairy/Digestive Issues 32
Soy 34
GMO Foods 34
Eating Out 36
B12 37
If Everyone Went Vegetarian for Just One Day, the U.S. Would Save: 38
Letter to My Children 39
In A Nutshell 40

Part Two

Recipes

Appetizers

Guacamole 43

Artichoke Spread 44

Artichokes Italian-Style a la Connie 44

A Colorful Pepper-Corn-and-Bean-Dip 45

Dressing 45

Pine Nut Pesto 45

Red Bell Pepper Spread 46

Marvelous Marinated Mushrooms 46

Eggplant and Zucchini Bruschetta 47

Traditional Tomato Bruschetta 48

Marinated Green Olive Nibbles 49

Kale Chips 49

Salads

Green-Beans-Tomatoes-and-Lots-of-Wonderful-Basil-Salad 51

Orange-Broccoli-Carrot-and-Raisin-Salad 51

Crunch-Salad with-Black-Eyed Peas 52

Peas, Shoe Peg Corn and Green Bean Salad 53

Wild Rice Pilaf 53

Mung Bean Salad 54

Barley-Corn-and-Kidney-Bean-Salad 55

Dressing 55

Tabouli - Tabbouleh - Taboli - Tabouleh - Taboule 56

Bulgur Wheat-Mint-Parsley-and-Cilantro-Salad (AKA Tabouli) 56

Wheatberry Salad 57

Corn and Avocado Salad 58

Southwestern Corn Salad ... 58

Cold, Refreshing Asparagus Salad ... 59
    Dressing ... 59

Everything-But-the-Kitchen-Sink-Salad ... 60

Cabbage Slaw ... 61

Mango Slaw ... 62
    Dressing ... 62

Strawberry-Mango Salad ... 62

Ramen Noodle Slaw Mix ... 63

Gazpacho ... 64

Entrees

Zucchini Crust Pizza With Lots of Wonderful Toppings ... 67

A-Hearty-No-Meat-Chock-Full-of-Vegetables-Good-For-You-Chili ... 68

Pasta with Mushrooms and Tomato Sauce ... 70

Split Peas and Pasta ... 71

Quinoa Paella without the Meat ... 72

Thai Noodles, Creamy and Peanutty ... 74

Pakoras ... 75

Curried Cickpea Croquettes with Salsa Verde ... 76

Salsa Verde ... 77

Beans and Rice ... 78

Tomato Salsa ... 78

Peas and Macaroni ... 80

Bean and Corn Casserole ... 81

Italian Pasta Sauce ... 82

Nutty-Couscous-with-Mint-and-Tomatoes ... 83
    Vinaigrette Dressing ... 83

Brown Rice with Corn and Peas ... 84

Brown Rice with Dill and Tomatoes ... 85
    Dressing ... 85

Spinach with Tomatoes and Potatoes ... 86

Collard Wraps ... 87

Breakfast Foods

Slightly-Nutty-Non-Dairy-No-Egg-Pancakes 90
Muesli 90
Fruit Smoothie, Delicious and Healthy 91
Chia Seed Pudding 92
Whole Oat Groat Oatmeal 92
Lemon Water 93
Various Egg Replacers 93

Sides

Roasted Potatoes 95
Broccoli Ala Orange 95
Flat Italian Green Beans and Tomatoes with Greek Seasoning 96
Baked Artichoke Hearts with Tomatoes & Onions 97
Tomatoes Filled with Minted Peas 98
Brown Rice Medley 99

Soups

Zopa de Tomate (Tomato Soup) 103
Thick-and-Creamy-No-Cream-Celery-Soup 104
Cauliflower and Leek Soup 105
Thick-and-Creamy-No-Cream-Broccoli-Soup 106
Corn Soup 106
Avocado Soup, Cold and Refreshing 107
Sherried-Carrot-Butternut-Squash-Soup 108
Cabbage Soup 109

Desserts

Brownies 111

Oatmeal-Raisin-Chewy-Cookies 112

Rhubarb-Apple Crisp 114

A Lovely Warm Fruit Mix to End the Meal 115

Lemon Cheesecake with Graham Cracker Crust 116
- Crust 116
- Filling 116

Nutty-Cinnamon-Bananas 118

Rum-Raisin-Bread Pudding, Rich, and Chocolatey 119

Part Three

One Week of Sample Menus

Day 1 124

Day 2 125

Day 3 125

Day 4 126

Day 5 126

Day 6 127

Day 7 128

Acknowledgements 129

Resources 130-133
- Books 130
- Websites 131
- DVDs 132

Endnotes 132-133

Index 134-145

Part One

Health and Wellness

An explanation of the connection and role that diet plays in preventing disease.

Introduction

A glorious spring day in Naples, today is. As I sit here writing, the bougainvillea are in brilliant bloom and the scent of gardenias and jasmine are wafting about me. A truly magnificent day. Sigh! I'm content when I encounter nature such as this.

And yet, on the other hand, I'm dismayed. I'm dismayed at what's going on around us in our society. Look at the sickness and death and obesity and suffering in our friends and loved ones. Taking to the knife for heart disease. Chemotherapy for cancer. Blindness and lost limbs as a result of diabetes. It's incredulous! The stunning part of all of this is that it doesn't have to happen. There are myriad studies and scientific facts that prove a diet with no animal products reverses and prevents countless diseases including heart disease, cancer, diabetes and a host of degenerative illnesses and conditions.

I am vegan, a whole-foods, plant-based eater, for preventative health matters as you will read within these pages. My family history is rife with heart disease, cancer and diabetes. The Research is in. Countries who do not eat the Standard American Diet (SAD)–animal products–do not suffer from the diseases that are prevalent in our country. We are getting too much of the wrong kind of protein, too much fat and too much cholesterol. Just stop and look around. We've all been touched in one way or another by one of these horrible diseases, not to mention obesity, lack of energy, aches and pains, dementia, Alzheimer's disease and on and on. Does it make sense then that it's what we're eating which is causing much of this?

The genetic predisposition to most common diseases is also hugely misunderstood by the general population. Yes, I have all of those diseases in my history. I am genetically predisposed. If I continue to eat the way my ancestors ate, chances are quite likely, I will succumb to the same diseases they did. However, if I change my ways now, chances are also quite good that I do *not* have to succumb to the same diseases. As Dr. Gary Null says, "We have an epidemic of *preventable* diseases." If they're preventable, why in God's Good Name would we NOT WANT to do what's been shown and proven to be healthier? Why? I'm perplexed!

I have been studying and researching this topic for several years. I have found, firmly believe and am highly convinced that diseases can not only be prevented but also be reversed by eating a whole-foods, plant-based diet. Don't take my word for it. Do your own research, but at least do it.

Why Vegan?

On a trip to Ecuador a few years ago, I was asked *Why Ecuador?* But that's another story. Similarly, and oftentimes, I am asked, *Why Vegan?* I think people, my family and friends, alike, thought I had gone straight off the deep-end or that maybe it was a fad with me. They couldn't believe I was doing something so radical, veer from what I had eaten my entire life, as to stop eating animal foods. I, myself, didn't think I would ever do anything like this, either. I'm a fairly grounded and balanced person. So, for me to change my way of eating to such a drastic extent may and did seem a bit extreme to others. So, people have watched me from a distance perhaps not thinking I could sustain this way of eating as I loved eating meat, chicken, fish, ice cream and the like, and ate the good old Standard American Diet and everything in it. I'm Italian. I love to eat. In fact, as my mother put it once, "We, as Italians, ***Live to Eat.*** Bill, my husband, on the other hand, ***Eats to Live."*** He does not enjoy food; neither do a couple of our children. They consider it an imposition if they have to stop doing what they're doing to eat because they are hungry. Foreign concept to me. There isn't much in the way of food that I do not like. I like to look at food, prepare it, talk about it, smell it, savor it going down, and even discuss a meal *after* I've eaten it. I am healthy, full of energy and feeling quite well, thank you and thank God.

This wasn't something I planned; it rather *just happened.* It all started with a book I'd read, *Brain Trust* by Colm Kelleher. The subtitle intrigued me: *The Hidden Connection Between Mad Cow and Misdiagnosed Alzheimer's Disease*. The book made such an impression on me and by the time I finished it, I was resigned to never eat beef or pork again. During the entire next year, still not eating any beef or pork, I continued to study, read, research, watch DVDs, attend seminars and talk with people, hearing many testimonies along the way. It had become quite a passion and a pass-time.

Bill and I, one evening, happened upon a PBS Special by Gary Null, PhD, nutritionist, scientist and lecturer. We sat mesmerized for two hours watching his lecture on health and how important it was for us to eat in a vegetarian manner. I truly had no intention of changing my way of eating. I really and truly did not; still, I was interested. I was learning and I was truly taken with what he had to say. Over the course of several months, we watched many health and food-related lectures.

One morning, about a year later, I woke up and a decision had nested in my mind. In addition to not eating beef and pork, I also was now going to stay away from chicken, fish, wheat, sugar and coffee. And that was really the beginning. It, indeed, just happened. Did Bill ride along with me? Not then, at least. But more on his story later.

And so, for several years now, I have not eaten any beef, pork, chicken or fish. I have not eaten eggs, butter, cheese nor have I consumed dairy in any form. That is, unless, of course, they show up hidden in foods when I am not aware—for example, when eating in restaurants or eating at the homes of others. When I am in control, however, I eat organic only and no animal products whatsoever. With all that I *don't eat,* I am often asked the question, *What DO you eat?*

Oh my goodness! There is a plethora of food without animal products that is absolutely delicious. Some I had never eaten nor had I been aware they even existed. And, yes! They are full of all the nutrients our bodies need to survive, contrary to the opinion of many.

I am also often asked the question, *Do you feel better?* Thank God I didn't feel bad. I had no health problems. This might seem curious to some, but I changed my way of eating strictly as a preventative measure. But I can tell you one thing. I have a huge appetite and can eat more than many people. I was full on many occasions but I was *never* satisfied. I thought I was eating healthily, but in an attempt to keep my weight in control, I purposely did not eat many foods such as potatoes, pasta, bread, and even fruit. Eating this way, I am now satisfied. I not only eat better and healthier, but also more in quantity, yet I can still keep my weight in check.

We are surrounded by health problems, one disease after another. I am dismayed that there are no cures for all the money pumped into research.

Americans eat only 5 percent of calories from fruits, vegetables, beans, and unprocessed nuts and seeds, the foods that contain the necessary nutrients to maintain normal health. Unless our diet is designed so our caloric consumption largely comes from these protective foods, we should not be surprised if our twenty-five year-old daughter develops lupus or our eighteen-year-old develops ulcerative colitis. Once they pass their child-bearing years, many of our children will be overweight; age rapidly; require drugs for hypertension, diabetes, and heart disease; have a heart attack; or die prematurely from cancer. This can be avoided. [1]

Treading lightly, I once asked my husband's oncologist if he believed diet and disease were related. He said he did. I asked if he ever spoke to his patients about it. His response, "I don't have time." You can take what you want from that statement. It made me angry. You don't have time? *First do no harm* and you don't have time?

Cancer and heart disease have similar causes. Cancer kills about 35 percent of all adult Americans, heart disease and stroke about 50 percent. The more years of nutritional abuse and the earlier in life the abuse begins, the higher the risk. [2]

Other doctors I have visited with my husband, so I can get the details, in helping to care for him, are disrespectful and rude to me. Further, many do not even look at me while I am there taking notes and asking questions. One doctor even admitted that yes, he was a "pill pusher." Those words verbatim. Another doctor, when I presented him with a chart of Bill's numbers gone down as a result of his following a low-fat, low animal way of eating, gave it a cursory look and popped it back to me. He didn't even have the courtesy of looking at the entire page.

Yet a third doctor promised he wouldn't give my husband a narcotic pain medication and that he would only give him an emergency dose. After his rudeness to me, I left his office in tears and waited 30 minutes in the car for Bill. When he came out, he had a prescription in hand for 30 Oxycontin---a narcotic and a very addictive drug. Thirty, mind you. Now, I ask, is that an emergency dose? Needless to say, I did not have it filled. How does one win when we have doctors who don't help us in our quest to do better than surgeries and pills? I can tell you what I want to do. And that is to take full responsibility for my own health and body. Go to doctors who will work *with* you not *against* you. With *you* and not *for* the drug industry. And if I am caring for others, I cannot in all good conscience allow them to follow blindly what doctors prescribe for them, as in the case of my husband who wanted and accepted my care.

Genetics

Genetics plays only a small portion in the equation. If you have the genetics and predisposition for certain diseases and continue to eat the Standard American Diet, chances are great that health problems will be prevalent. Some people eat well and are sick. Others do not eat well and are healthy. But eliminating a good deal of the saturated fat and sugar and processed foods that inundate our diets, even though we may have a genetic predisposition toward a particular disease, gives us a much better chance at healthy living.

Genes do not determine disease on their own. Genes function only by being activated, or expressed, and nutrition plays a critical role in determining which genes, good and bad, are expressed. [3]

My family history is such that there has been cancer, heart disease and diabetes. My mother is one of ten children. Nine of her siblings either have or had cancer, heart disease or diabetes. Her mother, my grandmother woke up one morning blind as a result of diabetes. Just like that. Overnight. Blind. Many of my aunts and uncles had peripheral neuropathy (nerve weakness in their legs which rendered walking difficult), and one of my uncles in his eighties had a leg amputated as a result of diabetes. My mother began to exhibit sugar problems in her nineties---so ten of ten in ill health in their later years. Count their parents, my grandparents and the number is 12 of 12. My mother is 95 and also has severe dementia, a result of clogged arteries to the brain.

Further, the diet that most diabetics are told they need to eat by their doctors and the American Diabetic Association, does not keep their sugar under control, does not prevent them from limb amputations and does not prevent blindness. Why then, would anyone follow it? Medications. Diets that don't work. And still they are sick. Maybe it's just me, but something doesn't make sense about all of this. Bill's doctor ordered him to see the diabetes counselor. She advocated all things I knew were just not right for him. We listened and left and did not follow what she recommended. As an aside, we have found doctors who will work with us and that's what I encourage you to do if you are on a quest to help yourself and not follow blindly what doctors advocate. PLEASE DO NOT FOLLOW BLINDLY.

Research shows that people of the same ethnic background have hugely varying disease rates depending on their environment. Dozens of studies have documented that as people migrate, they assume the disease risk of the country to which they move. They do not change their genes, and yet they fall prey to diseases and illnesses at rates that are rare in their homeland population. Furthermore, we have seen disease rates change over time so drastically that it is biologically impossible to put the blame on genes. [4]

There are doctors out there who not only *prevent* these diseases with their protocol, but also *reverse* them by using and advocating certain foods over others, and suggesting to their patients that they adopt a new lifestyle if they want to become and stay well. Heart disease is just one of the many diseases that is reversible. As Dr. John McDougall states, "Our arteries are not cement. They are tissue and given the right foods, the tissue heals."

Some doctors actually admit that they don't tell their patients about changing their diet and lifestyle because they feel the vast majority wouldn't go along with it anyway. Perhaps, the decision should be left to the patient. Even if only one in a hundred changed and became healthy because of the change, it would be worth it.

What You Think and How it Affects You

People say to me, I don't *want* to live to be 100. I'm going to enjoy eating what I want to eat and that's that. Naturally, none of us has the choice as to when we will die. My answer is always, it's not how long we live, but how long we live healthily. I've heard others caring for aging parents in nursing homes say, *When I get there.....* No! I am NOT going to a nursing home. I am just NOT. First of all, I am not going to invite that thought into my life by even verbalizing it. You know, we are what we think and we are what we eat. If we think we will, we will. If we think we won't, we won't. If we think we can, we can and if we think we can't we can't. Somewhere along the line, it comes down to our attitude. And also doing the things it takes to keep our bodies healthy.

Many years ago, the mother of the friend of my daughter, Mary Carol, just knew without a shadow of a doubt that she was going to die of back cancer because HER mother did. And, guess what? She did. She invited that very thought into her being and it became a reality. A 10 year old girl lost her mother because, I believe, she invited that belief into her system.

Families all across America are ravaged by diseases simply because we are being told the foods we are eating are good for us. It's what we've heard all our lives. Why wouldn't we believe it? Mainstream medicine doesn't seem to know either; after all, they're not educated in nutrition. On the other hand, those who do know are turning a deaf ear, all in the name of profits.

I am doing for my body the thing I think will keep it strong and healthy for as long as I live. It's what's right for me and for thousands of others who have traveled this road before me. We should all die of old age and not from the sicknesses that are so rampant today.

Other cultures, who eat differently than the good old SAD – Standard American Diet, prove this to be true.

My mother, for years, complained that she couldn't remember anything. She would be so frustrated that it became a mantra with her. "I

can't remember anything. I can't remember anything." I tried so hard to encourage her not to continue to say this. But she just couldn't seem to help herself. She said it so often, that eventually she *couldn't* remember anything, not even how to brush her hair or care for herself. It breaks my heart.

Change is Not Easy

People don't take to this way of eating very easily. We've been taught for so many years that eating meat and cheese and dairy is GOOD for us. Studies prove that this couldn't be further from the truth. Check it out. The vast majority of these studies are funded by the pharmaceutical industry, the dairy industry, the sugar industry and the beef industry. Yet, there is still that faction of people who have never heard this. It's a complete change and I dare say, many people resist change, including myself sometimes.

Bill and I were talking about this one evening and he says there are several types of people who fall into one category or another.

1. He says there are those like me who hear that the Standard American Diet (SAD) is what's causing many of our illnesses, degenerative diseases and obesity, and that there is another way. *Really????* People like me, say. Then, I won't eat that way any longer.

2. Then, there are those, like Bill for example, who has been open enough to studying along with me and *knows* and *believes* that this way of eating can create better health for us — to the tune of even *reversing* diseases. However, he and those like him, cannot seem to tear themselves away from the addiction of meat, cheese and dairy. Only when their backs are up against the wall, as in Bill's case, do they dare to make a change.

Over the last nine years, Bill has had a five-artery heart bypass, a stent in one of the same arteries a year later, face cancer, and recently diabetes diagnosed by one doctor and hypoglycemia diagnosed by another doctor. He has not been able to get his sugar numbers under control. They've been consistently high in the 200s at times. Of course, here I am having seen the ravages of diabetes in my own family and at his side suggesting he cut out meat, dairy and cheese.

Finally, he took the step and guess what? In two weeks, his sugar numbers have been consistently in the good range --- near 100 or slightly above or below. And, now, Macular Degeneration in one eye and vein occlusion in the other eye.

Further, one of the causes of Macular Degeneration is fat in the eye arteries. It stands to reason that if blocked arteries leading to our hearts will give us a heart attack and blocked arteries leading to our brain will give us a stroke and blocked arteries leading to other parts of our bodies are similarly affected, then it just makes sense that blocked arteries to the eyes can have a negative impact on our eyes (Dr. John McDougall). Another great reason to go Vegan.

3. The third category of person is one who says, "I like my meat and I'm going to continue to enjoy eating it." Those who espouse this philosophy may be healthy now, but the problem with this attitude is their later years are, in a great number of cases, severely compromised. If I may repeat, It doesn't have to be that way.

4. You've probably heard the phrase, *The roof doesn't leak until it rains*. Another category is the young. They feel they are bullet-proof, or they are not in ill health, in many cases, so they are not willing to make a change in the name of prevention.

> If you're willing to make the change, you have
> a great chance and a high probability that
> weight will come off and other maladies will be
> reversed. Give it a try for 90 days.

What do you have to lose besides unwanted weight and ill health?

Vegan vs. Vegetarian

You might ask, *What's the difference between being vegetarian and being vegan?* Basically, vegan is vegetarian without the dairy. However, some vegetarians eat chicken and fish, staying away from beef or pork only. Some do not eat beef, pork, chicken or fish but will eat dairy. Some eat tortilla chips and potato chips and junk food. This is not a true vegetarian diet, nor is it a healthy one.

Vegans, on the other hand, eat no meat or animal products of any kind, including no eggs or dairy whatsoever. Some vegans eat this way for ethical reasons. Some vegans eat this way for health reasons and some do it for a little of both. Those vegans who do it for the pure love of animals, will go so far as to not wear leather, silk or be associated with any by-product of animals.

Protein

Despite what many people think, it's not at all difficult for a vegan to consume the dietary recommendations for protein. It's the absolute first question people ask when they discover someone does not eat meat. This paranoia, actually, is quite out of order. Although our bodies certainly need protein for good and optimal function, we do not need the copious amounts we are getting in an animal diet. Contrary to popular opinion, less protein is actually better than more.

Yes, a vegan diet is lower in protein than an animal diet and studies show that our bodies actually require less than what was formerly thought. In fact, large amounts of animal protein unfortunately leaches calcium from our bones, actually causing osteoporosis.

Animal protein tends to cause calcium to pass through the kidneys and into the urine. In the process, calcium is not only lost, but it ends up in your urinary tract, where it can cause stones. [5]

There is a mountain of compelling research showing that "low-quality" plant protein, which allows for slow but steady synthesis of new proteins, is the healthiest type of protein. [6]

As long as your diet is varied: fruits, vegetables, nuts, seeds, beans, and grains, you will have plenty of protein in your diet. If you eat junk food and no animal products, you are essentially a vegan, but I dare say not a healthy one.

Whole, unrefined foods are totally and unequivocally necessary for one to obtain every necessary nutrient your body needs. That means fresh as much as absolutely possible. Stay away from anything boxed or refined and you'll be okay.

Good sources of protein are oatmeal, brown rice, nuts and seeds, tofu, grains, lentils, chick peas, beans, split peas and nearly all vegetables. Chia seeds also contain protein and can be made into a wonderful pudding that tastes like tapioca (it's in the recipe section). Quinoa (Pronounced keen-wah), a 5000 year-old tiny pasta-like grain is another great source of protein. If you eat a wide variety of plant-based foods, you will have sufficient protein in your diet. This is key: diversity of food.

Combining Foods

Contrary to popular opinion, it is very easy for a vegan diet to meet the recommendations for protein., as long as calorie intake is adequate. Strict protein combining is not necessary; it is more important to eat a varied diet throughout the day. [7]

Please refer to the following website for more information: http://www.vrg.org/nutrition/protein.htm#table1. Frances Moore Lappe, in her book *Diet for a Small Planet,* actually prescribed the complex process of combining of foods low in one amino acid with foods higher in other amino acids in order to get the proper protein mix. Lappe was actually being overly cautious to remain in line with those in the Nutrition fields.

She has since reversed her position on this : "In combating the myth that meat is the only way to get high quality protein, I reinforced another myth. I gave the impression that in order to get enough protein without meat, considerable care was needed in choosing foods. Actually it is much easier than I thought."[8] The American Dietetic Association, an organization that certifies dietitians and nutritionists, also concurs with this position. It simply is no longer necessary to combine foods to get sufficient protein requirements.

Mercury

Many of us are walking around with mercury levels in excess of what's considered to be safe. Many people have switched to more consumption of fish because it contains the high omega 3 fatty acids. However, the waters these fish swim in is highly polluted with mercury; consequently, many of these fish contain mercury. Those most polluted include shark, swordfish, king mackerel, tilefish, halibut and white albacore tuna (both canned and fresh). Despite the fact that you would get an excellent source of omega 3 fatty acids from these fish, Dr. David Perlmutter, and other health experts like him, recommend that we do not eat them. The fish with the lowest concentration of mercury are Alaskan Salmon, Tilapia, Haddock and Sardines. [9]

"We found that if people eat fish, the mercury level in their system goes up. They stop eating fish, the mercury level goes down. It's that simple. It's a documented poison. Wherever it's seen, it's been a problem." [10]

—Dr. Jane Hightower

When asked what he thinks is the single most important thing we can do to keep our brain functioning at its peak and prevent brain aging, Dr. Perlmutter says that we must be absolutely vigilant about what we put on our plates. Nutrition is *the* most important tool for staying

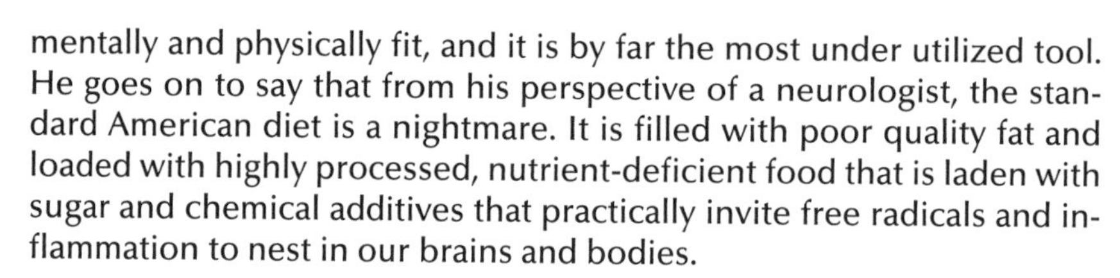

mentally and physically fit, and it is by far the most under utilized tool. He goes on to say that from his perspective of a neurologist, the standard American diet is a nightmare. It is filled with poor quality fat and loaded with highly processed, nutrient-deficient food that is laden with sugar and chemical additives that practically invite free radicals and inflammation to nest in our brains and bodies.

Fat is a vital nutrient for our brain and though we hear much about essential fatty acids, we tend to get more of the omega 6 fatty acids, than we do the omega 3 fatty acids. In fact, omega 3 deficiency is very prevalent among Americans and one common symptom is depression. Good sources of omega 3 fatty acids are dark green leafy vegetables, walnuts, pumpkin seeds, flaxseeds, and hempseeds. Avocados are another good source of omega 6 fatty acids.

Organic versus Conventional Foods

Organic foods are grown in purer, nutrient-dense soil than conventional foods. They contain more minerals and no chemicals or pesticides.

On one of our tours in Eucador, we learned a few things from another people and how they grow their food. An Associative Culture is a means by which they grow two plants together, also called a symbiotic relationship. For example, the corn needs nitrogen, so they plant beans next to the corn. The beans give nitrogen to the soil, yet they need to

wrap themselves around something. The corn is there for the beans to wrap themselves around and the bugs stay away from both.

Quinoa (pronounced keen-wah) is a bitter plant (thus you always need to rinse before cooking), consequently worms and insects instinctively stay away from it. By the same token, it is planted in close relationship to another plant that doesn't naturally fend off the bugs. In this way, the worms and insects stay away from that plant, as well. These are natural protectors for their plants. We could learn a thing or two from them.

But then, it's not about the nutrition, or the consumer or the desire to ward off diseases and stay healthy. It's big business and it's about profits and it's the reason we need to watch out for our own interests and our own bodies and our own good health.

The following chart shows the amount of minerals in organic food compared to conventional food: [11]

Calcium:	63 percent higher
Chromium:	78 percent higher
Iodine:	73 percent higher
Iron:	59 percent higher
Magnesium:	138 percent higher
Potassium:	125 percent higher
Selenium:	390 percent higher
Zinc:	60 percent higher

We have a wonderful market in our town, *Food and Thought,* where 100% of the foods are *certified organic*. I love it because absolutely everything in this store is organic, down to the paint on the wall. You don't have to sort through or read labels to determine if something is organic. Just by virtue of being in the store, you know it is.

There are several areas to the store. The grocery section is so laden with wonderful, brightly-colored, fresh produce that it makes me want to buy it all; there is a plethora of nuts, beans and grains all neatly packaged; shelves filled with health and recipe books, and a very long coffee/smoothie/juice bar where juices are made with 100% organic fruit.

Then there is a fresh-homemade-from-scratch-restaurant-area which serves breakfast, lunch and dinner. Their pancakes are made with sprouted flour, which digests as a vegetable. They properly soak all the beans for hours before they are cooked. They make soups with reverse osmosis water, never tap water, and they use the highest quality olive oil, never canola, soy or hydrogenated oils. They never use aluminum pots or pans or any with Teflon. A different Raw food choice is available everyday, as well.

I bought the Mock Salmon (sort of like a paté) one day and thought it was delicious. You wouldn't have known the difference. Later at home, I asked Bill if he wanted to try it and he did. His response? "It tastes just like fish, but not fishy-tasting." He proceeded to eat the rest of it as a snack on crackers. You must know Bill's eating habits by now. This is a real rarity for him. So, yes, there are ways of getting around food dislikes.

In addition to all of that, there is a nutritional supplement section, skin care, organic essential oils, laundry detergents and cleaning supplies, all green and environmentally friendly. Anyway, those of us who love to frequent this place feel it is a true blessing to have it in our midst. Thank you, Frank Oakes.

There is always that question, *Isn't organic more expensive?* It may be, but I don't think so. Besides, you are going to pay one way or the other. You will pay in doctor visits, medication and general overall ill health. I'd rather pay up-front for organic and feel quite confident that without all the chemicals, hormones, antibiotics, and pesticides that I am doing my body a favor and that it is better all the way around.

The foods in the large conventional grocery chains all look wonderful in their neatly stacked and saran wrapped packages, but how many people give thought to what these foods actually consist of? They are loaded with pesticides and the milk, eggs and meats are filled with hormones and antibiotics. It's all about appearance and shelf life, not about what's best for us.

I am very disappointed if I can't get organic when I'm away from home.

Weight Loss

Who doesn't need to lose a few pounds or more? As I'm sure you know, obesity is rampant among us.

One-third of our population is obese. [12] Not only that, but a worse scenario is the escalating number of overweight and obese children. About 15% of America's youth (ages six to nineteen) are overweight. Another 15% are at risk of becoming overweight. [13]

And when children as young as six are asking how they can lose their tummies and preteens wanting to go on a diet, something is seriously wrong.

I was always trying to lose the proverbial five pounds. Instead of losing, I actually gained. Five pounds here and another five pounds there until I had way more weight on me than I wanted or felt good about. I wasn't considered fat, but I didn't like the extra weight as I had always been very thin. It's true! It was an obsession with me, and I knew it. I finally found the answer to not only a healthier body, but also a thinner one.

Some people can eat and eat all they want and still maintain their weight loss. I must say, that even though vegan, and even though I eat way more than I ever did before, I do need to watch my portions to maintain my weight. I have a huge, ravenous appetite and did I mention before, *I Love to Eat?!*

It's not about metabolism as we so often hear. Added weight doesn't necessarily have to go along with aging. You can get older without putting on unwanted pounds if you eat the right foods: Whole, unrefined, unprocessed and in as natural a state as you can get it. I and many vegans like me are proof positive!

People ask me all the time, "What do you eat?"

In the recipe section which follows, you will see the wide variety of foods that I eat. At least once every two weeks, I will make the Black-eyed pea salad. It's crunchy, delectable and contains a variety of vegetables. This recipe makes a lot, so what I don't package up and give to my children, I have several meals of for the week. It makes a great and quick luncheon dish or one of many sides combined to make a full meal.

Another wonderful salad is one made by a friend of Mary Carol's that he has made for me several times. In fact, he made a large bowl and gave it to me on my birthday last week. He juliennes Granny Smith Apples, Jicama, cucumbers, red, yellow and green peppers, and mixes it all with a vinaigrette dressing. Yum! Another wonderful crunchy and varied salad.

I eat fruit in the morning. Perhaps later in the morning I will have a small bowl of whole grain or steel cut oatmeal with either no milk or Almond Milk sweetened with a bit of Agave Nectar. You could also add some raisins, cranberries nuts or bananas. There you have it: a filling and healthy breakfast. The vegan pancakes are just great. Kennedy & Kerigan ask for these whenever they are with me. Though these are great, they are not for everyday if you are watching your weight especially.

For lunch or a just a mid-day snack, I will steam a large container or bag of organic spinach to which I have added salt, pepper and garlic powder. I even drink all of the juice. How good and healthy is that?

Or, I will shred white and purple cabbage, peel and cut up a mango, add some pumpkin seeds or pine nuts, drizzle a little Agave sweetener and salt and pepper and I have a very satisfying lunch dish.

In just a matter of minutes, less than an hour for sure, I can make a hearty and filling soup. Check out the celery or the tomato soups. Any one of these soups with a salad is another great lunch or dinner meal.

For dinner I will have a large mixed green salad with corn, black beans, olives, pumpkin seeds, tomatoes, cucumbers, sprouts, peppers, artichoke hearts and the like. Whatever I might have in the refrigerator or pantry. Just the other evening, I made a tabouli salad, fresh green beans steamed with a little sea salt and a green salad. It was plenty filling and tasted delicious.

You could also bake a sweet potato or an Idaho potato. Sprinkle just a bit of sea salt and eat it plain. I don't, but if you had to have butter, use vegan butter sparingly, for a bit of flavor.

The meatless chili, the bean burritos, and other entrees such as The Creamy Thai Noodles with peanut sauce in the recipe section are worthy enough for guests. I top the chili with guacamole and/or homemade salsa and it is better than any dish I can get in a restaurant. Plus, I know exactly what's in it (no hidden foods). It's fresh, organic and pure. Take a good look at the recipe section and you will see that you will not go hungry.

Five of my friends and I have a Girls' Get-together once a month at our homes. We each take turns hosting. The one who hosts prepares the entree and a salad and the others bring the sides. Though they are not vegans, they are intent on eating healthy. They are extremely accommodating to me, always preparing recipes with me in mind. We all usually go back for seconds because the food is SO blessed good. Again, and we comment on this all the time: You just don't get meals like this in a restaurant!

Sugar and Artificial Sweeteners

As wonderfully delicious as sweets can be, sugar and things made from refined white sugar are among the worst things we can put in our bodies. There was a time growing up and even into my adulthood, when a meal wasn't complete without a dessert at the end. If there were no desserts per se, we had to have at least a few cookies. Even a graham cracker would do. We were also known to have donuts and pastries and cherry pie and cakes for breakfast. The body is a wonderful thing. It takes such abuse and yet can be so good to us. All that abuse does take its toll though. Our bodies have to work overtime to process sugar and in the meantime, precious nutrients are lost, thereby playing havoc with our immunity.

Sugar hampers several vital immune system functions, including white blood cell migration and phagocytosis, which is the ability of white blood cells to eliminate bacteria, viruses and other infectious intruders. Plus sugar can contribute to the gradual depletion of minerals needed for healthy bones and teeth. [14]

It's so highly processed and refined that there is nothing healthful about it whatsoever. It's a never-ending cycle. The more we eat, the more we crave. It has a mild drug-like effect. That is, it affects the brain in essentially the same way as opiate drugs; this effect helps explain why people crave sugar, especially during times of stress. [15]

If you transition to a whole-foods diet, you won't crave sweets. I know. I've been a sweet eater all my life and I rarely eat them today. When I do feel the need, a piece of fruit usually fills the bill. When I do, from time to time, indulge in sweets, and it's mostly a social or impulsive thing, I can tell the difference immediately. I am bloated, stuffed and do not feel very well. Same goes for breads and food made from white flour which all act in the body the same as sugar.

The thing to remember is simply to avoid sugars at all costs since they cause the pancreas to overproduce insulin. They also lack B vitamins and other essential nutrients found in complex carbohydrates that are needed to metabolize sugar into energy. [16]

As I tell my family, as bad as sugar is, artificial sweeteners are even worse. Even Splenda? Even Splenda. Splenda actually contains chlorine and isn't any better than the other artificial sweeteners. Aspartame, under the names of Equal and Nutrasweet, is full of chemicals. I stay as far away from these as possible. There was a time I did have them in my house, but several years ago when I discovered how terrible they were, I disposed of every single packet. More recently, we've been hearing about Truvia. It's a play on words made to sound like Stevia (the good sweetener), and in truth is chemically made and no better than the other artificial sweeteners on the market.

"With each sip of diet soda, EVERY user gets a micro-dose of three poisons, two of which (formaldehyde and formic acid) are known carcinogens....along with that side-order of DKP, the tumor agent." [17]

You can't even find a package of gum on the market without Aspartame in it. Why would they need to put Aspartame in a gum that is not sugar-free? It's in thousands of our foods. Read the labels and you will see just how many.

Aspartame came onto the market in 1983. Funnily enough, in 1984, there was a 10% jump in brain tumors completely unexplained by the neurological profession. [18] Just in our own little family circle we know at least three people who have had brain tumors. Two have since died and one had major brain surgery and is still suffering the effects.

It's a silent killer and has subtle, long-term toxic effects which do a slow accumulation in the body. Aspartame is a chemical and turns into methyl ester once ingested. When the body breaks down aspartame it turns into wood alcohol and is then broken down into formaldehyde. Yes, formaldehyde is a by-product of aspartame. Studies show that Aspartame causes brain tumors in mice and the Delaney Act states that anything that causes tumors in animals should not be approved for human use. There were no studies done on Aspartame in England, yet it was approved. And because England put their stamp of approval on it, it was approved around the world.

Some people have more of a sensitivity to toxins and are more affected than others. Yet, there are those who don't notice anything. It's too much of a chance to take to save a few calories, in my humble opinion.

The above information on Aspartame has been taken from the film, Sweet Misery: A Poisoned World. For more information on this, please go to Dorway.com and google The Bressler Report.

The Bressler Report is the text of an FDA Report on Searle Laboratories documenting experimental studies of Aspartame on Animals. The FDA Report was released as a result of the Freedom of Information Act. Noted on this report was "FDA tables gutted" as were several pages, text and memos before it was released. One wonders why this information was removed before the document was released and what the FDA did not want the public to learn.

For more than fifteen years, Betty Martini of Mission Possible, an organization she founded and runs non-stop, has given her time, effort and energy to inform people that the CDC has been less than truthful regarding the safety of Aspartame and that "it is a toxic poison unfit for human consumption....a slow neurotoxin that is especially bad for diabetics." In one day she received 12,000 case histories of people suffering from Aspartame that her computer crashed.

The following are just a few of the FDA recognized symptoms (that required a Freedom of Information Act request to obtain from them), people have suffered when ingesting Aspartame. When discontinuing use, symptoms abate or disappear altogether:

Abdominal pain, anxiety attacks, arthritis, Asthma, Asthmatic Reactions, Bloating, Edema (fluid retention), Blood Sugar Control Problems (Hypoglycemia or Hyperglycemia, Brain Cancer (Pre-approval studies in animals), Breathing difficulties, burning eyes or throat, Burning Urination, Can't think straight, Chest pains, Chronic cough, Chronic Fatigue, Confusion, Death, Depression, Diarrhea, Dizziness, Excessive thirst or Hunger, Fatigue, Feel unreal, Flushing of face, Hair Loss (Baldness) or Thinning of Hair, Hearing Loss, Heart Palpitations, Hives, Hypertension (High Blood Pressure), Impotency and Sexual Problems, Inability to concentrate, Infection Susceptibility, Insomnia, Irritability, Itching, Joint Pains, laryngitis, "Like thinking in a fog," Marked personality changes, Memory Loss, Menstrual Problems or Changes, Migraines and Severe Headaches, Muscle spasm, Nausea or Vomiting, Numbness or Tingling of Extremities, Other Allergic-like Reactions, Panic Attacks, Phobias, poor memory, Rapid Heart Beat, Rashes, Seizures and Convulsions, Slurring of Speech, Swallowing Pain, Tachycardia, Tremors, Tinnitus, Vertigo, Vision Loss, Weight gain.

Aspartame Disease mimics symptoms or worsens the following Diseases: Fibromyalgia, Arthritis, Multiple Sclerosis (MS), Parkinson's Disease, Lupus, Multiple Chemical Sensitivities (MCS), Diabetes and Diabetic Complications, Epilepsy, Alzheimer's Disease, Birth Defects, Chronic Fatigue Syndrome, Lymphoma, Lyme Disease, Attention Deficit Disorder (ADD), Panic Disorder, Depression and other Psychological Disorders.

Most people do not connect these symptoms with Aspartame. If you are suffering from any of these symptoms, give it up and do a sixty day test. Do not use any Aspartame for that length of time. If your symptoms disappear, you can probably rest assured they were caused by Aspartame.

"Aspartame is a Pandora's box of chameleon-like toxic chemicals, that causes cumulative physical and mental damage that hammer the unsuspecting victim into the ground... micro-dose by micro-dose!"

—The Bressler Report

What CAN we use as a sweetener?

Agave Nectar is a plant based sweetener and does not affect the glycemic index. Still, it doesn't mean you can go wild with it. I use Agave in recipes that call for sugar. Or, you can use maple syrup, or brown rice syrup. I have also used Evaporated Sugar Cane Juice but it's still sugar. Its name is misleading as it is a solid, unrefined sugar. Comes in a bag like refined sugar does. Fruit can also be used as a sweetener on your cereal. Stevia, an herb, can be used with safety, although, unlike some of my friends, I find that it has a bitter taste. If you can get past the bitterness, it's probably the best sweetener for your health.

"At one time the FDA actually embargoed Stevia and the rumor is Monsanto wants to add a molecule so they can patent it, and sell it themselves." [19] We should all be outraged about this.

Author Note:

As this book went to press, new information has surfaced on Agave Sweetener. Unfortunately, it seems there has been a marketing hype with it.

It also appears, according to some and Dr. Mercola in particular (Mercola.com), that Agave contains more high fructose corn syrup than fructose corn syrup. It does have a low-glycemic index, but is detrimental in other ways.

As reported by Dr. Ingrid Kohlstadt, a fellow of the American College of Nutrition and an associate faculty member at Johns Hopkins School of Public Health: "Agave is almost all fructose, a highly processed sugar with great marketing."

I have included this sweetener in many recipes within this book. Please research this on your own and if you decide to use Agave, use it very sparingly and seek it out from a reputable, organic company (there are a very few) rather than one of the companies that chemically produce it.

I continue to use it myself, but in extremely small amounts and not on a daily basis. Further, I buy only organic.

Fats

Many people stay away from beef and eat mostly chicken and fish thinking they are getting a healthier dose of nutrition and less fat. When I asked Dr. John McDougall about eating fish, his comment was, "Fish and chicken both are loaded with fat and cholesterol (not to mention the mercury in the fish), and eventually they take their toll on the body." In actuality, fish and chicken are no better than red meat. Better for your body to stay away from them all.

Fat is a vital nutrient for our brain and though we hear much about essential fatty acids, we tend to get more of the Omega 6 fatty acids than we do the Omega 3 fatty acids.

The best way to get the right kind and amount of fat in your diet is to skip animal products, fried foods, and oily foods and get your nutrition from vegetables, fruits, beans, and whole grains. Does it really matter whether or not we avoid animal products and added oils? Absolutely. A typical North American or European diet might provide 80 to 100 grams of fat per day, or even more. Switching from beef to modest portions of chicken and fish, will only trim this to about 60 grams. But setting animal products aside and avoiding added oils can drop this number closer to 20 grams. In the process, your cholesterol intake, which would be well over 200 milligrams per day on an unmodified diet, will drop to zero. Zero! Every cell in your body will thank you. [20]

Good sources of Omega 3 fatty acids are dark green leafy vegetables, walnuts, pumpkin seeds, flax seeds and chia seeds. Avocados are another good source of Omega 3s.

Good Carbs vs. Bad Carbs

As I mentioned earlier, before I changed my way of eating, I stayed away from potatoes, sweet potatoes, brown rice, and such because I thought all those carbs? They would put weight on me, for sure. No way. However, as I have come to learn, these are the good carbs, the complex carbohydrates, and for several years now, I have eaten them with no weight gain. Further, they are whole, unrefined, natural foods that will not raise your triglycerides. I only eat whole wheat pasta or brown rice pasta. These are not whole foods, so eat them sparingly. However, there are many kinds of pastas on the market to fill that need if you like it so much that you just can't stay away from it. The whole grains are ever the healthier and nutritious. They have not been robbed of their vital nutrients by removing the bran and the germ. Protein and many of the nutrients become completely non-existent in the refining of the flours.

Whole grains such as whole wheat, bulgur, quinoa, oatmeal, kamut, rye and pumpernickel contain all three parts (bran, germ, and endosperm), the healthiest and most nutritional elements. Ingesting bran, the rich, outer, protective fibrous layer and the germ are crucial to reaping highest nutritional values. Furthermore, eating whole grains can help prevent cancer, heart disease, constipation and diabetes. Whole grains are often a more valuable source of minerals, antioxidants and phyto-chemicals, than fruits and vegetables. Due to their remarkable ability to prevent chronic disease, weight gain, and high cholesterol, whole grains are essential to living longer, healthier lives. A few ways to integrate whole grains into your diet include whole grain spelt flour pastas, whole-wheat angel hair and artichoke flour pasta, which are all high in protein and fiber [21], and in my opinion every bit as good as the refined flour pastas.

Complex and unrefined carbohydrates are not only excellent sources of nutrients and fiber but they also keep the sugar from moving into the bloodstream too quickly because they are more slowly absorbed by the body. This is a special benefit for people with diabetes.

Carbohydrates do not cause diabetes. And a diet that focuses on keeping carbohydrates out of your diet is not a powerful way to manage---let alone reverse---the disease. If anything, healthy complex carbohydrates help prevent it. In fact, researchers found that people in countries who ate considerably more carbohydrates (starchy foods of grains, vegetables, bean dishes and noodles) than North Americans or Europeans do, diabetes was relatively rare. [22]

So, consuming more unrefined carbohydrates such as whole oats and oat bran helps lower blood cholesterol. With heart disease being the number one killer in the United States (Cancer is vying for the spot, I might add), it would behoove us all to eat our foods in a more natural and unrefined state.

Of all the carbohydrate groups, complex carbohydrates are probably the most beneficial to human metabolism. The time required to break down a complex carbohydrate minimizes the risk of overloading the body with a blast of sugar and a sudden release of insulin from the pancreas. A complex carbohydrate may, in fact, take hours to convert to glucose, rather than the few minutes required for processing a simple sugar. [23]

Westernized countries such as North America and Europe have a great incidence of intestinal problems likely due to their lack of unrefined whole grains in their diet. Problems such as diverticulosis, a common intestinal disorder, hemorrhoids, and colon cancer are more prevalent likely due to diets made up significantly of unrefined. whole grains. [24]

Cut out all together or at the very least minimize to a great extent your consumption of refined sugar, and anything refined and white: flour, pasta and rice. Look for whole grains in the cereal section, as well as the less familiar ones such as quinoa, barley, millet and lentils and wild rice, too.

Osteoporosis / Calcium / Dairy / Digestive Issues

American women have been consuming an average of two pounds of milk per day for their entire lives, yet 30 million American women have osteoporosis. Drinking milk does not prevent bone loss. Bone loss is accelerated by ingesting more protein than the body requires. [25]

Osteoporosis is caused by a number of things, one of the most important being too much dietary protein. [26] In other words, consuming too much animal protein leaches the calcium from our bones. Important also to note that the countries with the highest rates of osteoporosis, such as the United States, England and Sweden, also have the highest milk consumption.

The lactose (milk sugar) that makes up fully 55 percent of the calories in fat-free milk causes many people to have gas, cramps, and diarrhea. Lactose intolerance was once thought to be abnormal, but it is now known to be the biological norm; many people do not make the connection between their digestive symptoms and milk products. Besides being mucous forming, milk is also known to cause intestinal discomforts. Milk and dairy including cheese has been known to cause us a whole host of issues including nasal congestion, respiratory, sinus infections, asthma and constipation, diarrhea, fatigue and other intestinal related issues. [27] Note that mucous causes inflammation and inflammation causes disease. If you want to avoid disease, stay away from mucous forming foods.

I can speak from personal experience regarding the milk issue. I had intestinal issues throughout my entire childhood, but I had no idea what the cause was. I drank milk everyday and didn't really come to any conclusions as to why I had these issues. I was in my twenties and pregnant for our first child and the doctor had me watching my weight advising me to drink skim milk (I had always consumed whole milk). Well! Let me tell you! The less fat in it for me was the clincher; my symptoms were worse than ever. I was in misery. It was only then that I concluded it was the milk. I later learned that what was left behind was sugar---dairy sugar. When I eliminated milk completely from my diet, my symptoms cleared up to some extent.

Interestingly, when I over indulged at Christmas time and ate the many Italian Cookies and homemade fudge and everything "sugar," I suffered for days afterwards. When I stopped eating animal products, my digestive system became completely normal.

One of our sons went through the same torture as a child. We are led to believe we SHOULD have dairy. No one ever told us, or do they tell us now, that it could affect us in a negative way. Our two granddaughters, both suffer from dairy issues, as well. It seemed every time we were out to dinner, one had a stomach ache while the other was constantly clearing her throat. As mentioned, milk and cheese are severely mucous-forming. Age and experience does help. As I grew older, I became a quicker learner and deduced it was the dairy. Surely enough, these out of their diet, stomach aches and the clearing of the throat ceased to a great extent. The dairy and mucous issues affect some people worse than others. Another of our sons will NOT give up eating cheese and drinking milk and so he continues to suffer from an inability to breathe.

Good milk substitutes are Almond milk, brown rice milk, oat milk and hemp milk. There are ice cream alternatives, but they are rife with sugar. They are okay in a pinch but nothing tastes as good as the real thing. Ice cream, being dairy, was out of the question for me anyway, so I do not consume it, both for physical reasons and as a preventative measure.

Good sources of calcium are spinach, kale, chickpeas, broccoli, sesame seeds, Swiss chard, red leaf lettuce. Dried figs and dried apricots also contain calcium as well as orange juice and chia seeds.

Soy

Some people rely on Soy Milk and soy products, but I do not. There is a huge soy controversy. I have used soy sauce in some recipes but for the most part, I stay away from it as much as possible.

For starters, it is not good for the thyroid and it's difficult to digest. It suppresses the immune system and is known to contain a plethora of very dangerous chemical toxins, a fact of which many people are unaware.

Soy is highly estrogenic and has been known to cause growth problems in children. It interferes with protein digestion. It has the potential to cause infertility and to promote breast cancer, hypothyroidism and thyroid cancer. It has been connected to autoimmune thyroid disease and also interferes with the body's absorption of B12 and Vitamin D. Soy foods contain aluminum in great quantities which is a poison to the nervous system and the kidneys. These are just a few of the disorders connected to the intake of soy.

"Infants exclusively fed soy based formula have 13,000 to 22,000 times more estrogen compounds in their blood than babies fed Milk-based formula, the estrogenic equivalent of at least five birth control pills a day." http://www.panacea-bocaf.org/soyonlineservice.htm.

Soy contains natural Trypsin inhibitors and Trypsin is a part of the pancreatic enzymes that kills tumor tissue. Avoid soy at all costs.

For more information on the soy controversy, please visit: www.soyonlineservice.nz.

GMO Foods

Soy is also one of the more widely known Genetically Modified Foods. Here, the big monopolies are playing with Nature. They take genes from one species and put them into an entirely different species.

For example, Flounder genes have been injected into tomatoes so they will thrive in cold water. Genetically engineered hormones are injected into U.S. dairy cows to stimulate milk production. Soybeans, Corn and Canola oil are the major GM foods. These foods are experimental and millions of us are eating them and don't even realize it. GM Foods are a book unto themselves.

However, here are a few items taken from *Spilling the Beans Newsletter*, *newsletter@responsibiletechnology.org., used by permission:*

- The American Academy of Environmental Medicine called on Physicians to educate their patients, the medical community, and the public to avoid GM foods when possible and provide educational materials concerning GM food and health risks." They conclude, "There is more than a casual association between GM foods and adverse health effects. There is causation.
- More and more doctors are already prescribing GM-free diets. Dr. Amy Dean, a Michigan internal medicine specialist, and board member of AAEM says, "I strongly recommend patients eat strictly non-genetically modified foods." Ohio allergist Dr. John Boyles says, "I used to test for soy allergies all the time, but now that soy is genetically engineered, it is so dangerous that I tell people never to eat it." Dr. Jennifer Armstrong, President of AAEM, says, "Physicians are probably seeing the effects in their patients, but need to know how to ask the right questions. World renowned biologist Pushpa M. Bhargava goes one step further. After reviewing more than 600 scientific journals, he concludes that genetically modified organisms (GMOs) are a major contributor to the sharply deteriorating health of Americans.
- The experience of *actual* GM-fed experimental animals is scary. When GM soy was fed to female rats, most of their babies died within three weeks.
- GM corn and cotton are engineered to produce their own built-in pesticide in every cell. When bugs bite the plant, the poison splits open their stomach and kills them.
- Skin prick tests show some people react to GM, but not to non-GM soy. Soon after GM soy was introduced to the UK, soy allergies skyrocketed by 50%. Perhaps the US epidemic of food allergies and asthma is a casualty of genetic manipulation.
- The only published human feeding study revealed what may be the most dangerous problem from GM foods. The gene inserted into GM soy transfers into the DNA of bacteria living inside our intestines *and continues to function*. This means that long after we stop eating GMOs, we may still have potentially harmful GM proteins produced continuously inside of us. Put more plainly, eating a corn chip produced from Bt corn might transform our intestinal bacteria into living pesticide factories, possibly for the rest of our lives. When evidence of gene transfer is reported at medical conferences around the US, doctors often respond by citing the huge increase of gastrointestinal problems among their patients over the last decade.
- Scientists at the Food and Drug Administration (FDA) had warned about all these problems even in the early 1990s. According to documents released from a lawsuit, the scientific consensus at the agency was the GM foods were inherently dangerous, and might create hard-to-detect allergies, poisons, gene transfer to gut bacteria, new diseases, and nutritional problems.
- AAEM states, "GM foods have not been properly tested" and "pose a serious health risk." Not a single human clinical trial on GMOs has been published.

- Citizens need not wait for the results before taking the doctors advice to avoid GM foods. People can stay away from anything with soy or corn derivatives, cottonseed and canola oil, and sugar from GM sugar beets—unless it says organic or "non-GMO."

If even a small percentage of people choose non-GMO brands, the food industry will likely respond as they did in Europe—by removing *all* GM ingredients. Thus, AAEM's non-GMO prescription may be a watershed for the US food supply.

Eating Out

Sometimes eating in restaurants or at the homes of others who are not sensitive to your eating can be difficult. I am really blessed. I have friends, though not vegan, who are trying to eat healthier and are wonderful to accommodate me whenever they prepare meals at their homes.

Sometimes it takes a little longer to order in a restaurant because I question many of the dishes on the menu. One chef in a very fine and popular restaurant sputtered his feelings to the server, *If she wants pasta, tell her to go down the street.* And this attitude prevailed despite the fact that we had called two days ahead for a birthday party of eleven and especially asked if we would be able to get a vegan meal and were assured that we could. Chefs are creative and it would have taken nothing for him to prepare something with a two day notice. Obviously, he was an angry person. Needless to say, we have not returned to this restaurant.

On the other hand, a couple of times, the chefs actually came to my table and asked me to explain to them what I needed and wanted, and then added, no problem. Bless their hearts. For the most part, chefs will accommodate special requests. Just recently at one of the Disney Restaurants, **Portobello at Downtown Disney,** I had another experience. When I asked the server if what I was ordering had any cheese in it, he asked if I just didn't eat it or was I allergic to it. The chef came out and talked with me. The two managers on duty, one when we came in, Dana, and one as we left, Jennifer, both came to our table and they couldn't have been more accommodating. The server even went so far as to let me know that one of the appetizers on the antipasto tray had buttermilk in it. Well! We were all just dumbfounded that they took this extra special care. Will we go back there? You bet.

On another occasion, at a different restaurant an amusing incident happened when I mentioned to a young woman server that I was a vegan. She left and returned a few minutes later and asked, "What kind of disease did you say you have?" That left us all smiling.

Though some people don't know, most people in restaurants are aware of what a vegan is. Still, I have learned from experience and usually don't go into detail. I look at the menu and head straight for the sides that come with the entrees. If certain ingredients are available for their regular dishes, chances are, you can order a plate of these very sides. Sometimes, these dishes are incorporated with beef stock, cream, butter or cheese, so I always ask to be sure. Would it hurt if I had any of these items once in a while and not make it an issue when dining out? Probably not, but "once in a while" could turn into an everyday occurrence if you aren't vigilant. I have a conviction and I could make an excuse every time I eat if I wanted to. I choose not to make excuses. I choose to remain true to myself. I'm polite when I ask and if they can't accommodate me, I have a salad. It's really very simple.

B12

This is an extremely important nutrient for our nervous system and our neurological system, just to name a couple of necessary areas where it is needed for optimal health. Those new to veganism can exist on stores for at least three years. Then, you will need to monitor yourself to be sure you are getting enough. If you've ever heard that you need to eat animals to get sufficient B12, it simply is not true. Where do you think the animal gets its B12? From the plants they eat. Yes, B12 is in a plant-based diet. It's very rare to be deficient from Vitamin B12. Those who are deficient are also severely malnourished.

Although vitamin B12 is found in animal foods, it is not synthesized by plants or animals. Only bacteria make biologically active vitamin B12; animal tissues store "bacteria synthesized B12." [28]

An otherwise healthy strict vegetarian's risk of developing a disease from B12 deficiency by following a sensible diet is extremely rare---less than one chance in a million. [29]

You can also get more B12 by consuming nutritional yeast, not to be confused with brewer's yeast and it's also found in Nori seaweed. Mainstream medicine will have you believe that your body needs more than it actually needs to maintain good health. For awhile, I did supplement with B12 but then realized I didn't really require the extra I was taking. I have my blood monitored on a regular basis to be sure I am getting what I need in the foods I eat. So just be aware.

Those foods I eat consist of whole foods, a necessary aspect to being a healthy vegan. You can give up meat and animal products and be vegan. In my experience, though, I have known unhealthy, overweight vegans and vegetarians. It's important to remember to eliminate white flour, white sugar and any processed foods. If you eat whole grains, and whole fruits and vegetables, and as organic as possible, you can be confident you will be a healthy vegan.

There is a plethora of information by extremely credible medical doctors on the consequences of eating animal products. There are also studies galore and mountains of evidence that prove the case. Going vegan not only helps the planet and saves the animals, it can also prevent and reverse diseases. The literature is out there. One need only do a little research.

If Everyone Went Vegetarian for Just One Day, the U.S. Would Save:

The following excerpt is from Howard Lyman's Mad Cowboy Newsletter. And he very-edited it from the link below (Used by permission). Howard Lyman grew up on a dairy farm, became a cattle rancher and then a vegan when he discovered the ill effects of eating meat and its by-products.

Eye Opening Statistics

- 100 billion gallons of water, enough to supply all the homes in New England for almost 4 months;
- 1.5 billion pounds of crops otherwise fed to livestock, enough to feed the state of New Mexico for more than a year;
- 70 million gallons of gas -- enough to fuel all the cars of Canada and Mexico combined with plenty to spare;
- 3 million acres of land, an area more than twice the size of Delaware;
- 33 tons of antibiotics.

According to Environmental Defense, if every American skipped one meal of chicken per week and substituted vegetarian foods instead, the carbon dioxide savings would be the same as taking more than half a million cars off of U.S. roads. See how easy it is to make an impact?

Globally, we feed 756 million tons of grain to farmed animals. As Princeton bioethicist Peter Singer notes in his new book, if we fed that grain to the 1.4 billion people who are living in abject poverty, each of them would be provided more than half a ton of grain, or about 3 pounds of grain/day -- that's twice the grain they would need to survive. And that doesn't even include the 225 million tons of soy that are produced every year, almost all of which is fed to farmed animals. He writes, "The world is not running out of food. The problem is that we -- the relatively affluent -- have found a way to consume four or five times as much food as would be possible, if we were to eat the crops we grow directly." [30]

Letter to My Children

> *"I make myself rich by making my wants few."*
> —Thoreau

Many summers ago, I read the book, The Food Revolution by John Robbins. I wanted to share everything I had read in it with my children. I took notes on nearly all the chapters and then wrote them this letter:

Dear Children,

I have just finished reading a truly staggering and terrifying book, another one by John Robbins (the Robbins of Baskin-Robbins) whom as you know gave up his entire ice cream fortune because of the health implications. It is called The Food Revolution: How Your Diet Can Help Save Your Life and Our World

Past experience tells me that you will probably not read this book. And it is virtually impossible for me to verbally tell you what I've read. So, I've made it my mission for now to take notes on what I've read. I fervently hope you will read these notes. Some are verbatim. This also includes a part of your health history.

PRINT THIS OUT: Take these notes along on a plane ride, or in the car when you are waiting or in Dr. offices or wherever you have time on your hands. BUT PLEASE DO READ THEM. I want you to know what I have learned through ALL of my readings, and I want you to strive toward better health. You are all feeling well now, but you can see the health destruction around you.

Look at Nana Josephine. Her memory loss has declined so horribly, it truly distresses me. That memory loss is in our genes. She comes from a family of 10 and to my knowledge, none of her siblings have or had a memory problem. But they all had/have something else. Everyone of the ten have either had or have diabetes (Uncle Pete just had his leg amputated as a result), heart disease and cancer. Everyone one of them including Grandma and Grandpa Gerace.

The same holds true for Nanu's side: Diabetes, cancer and heart disease. Dad's father, PaPa, died of congestive heart failure. Nana Grace had cancer. IT'S IN YOUR GENES. LET'S DO SOMETHING GOOD FOR OURSELVES TO STOP IT FROM INVADING OUR BODIES. NOT TO SAY IT STILL COULDN'T HAPPEN, BUT OUR CHANCES WOULD BE GREATER FOR GOOD HEALTH. If we keep eating the Standard American Diet, chances are such that with all these diseases in the background, we could also succumb. The good news is we don't have to if we eat properly no matter that the diseases are part of our history.

I think I have counted that I had more than 30 aunts and uncles. Of the 30, six are still living. Of the six, 4 are failing MISERABLY. Grandma Gerace went blind as a result of diabetes. Aunt Bernice (though not a biological relative) is 99% blind as a result of diabetes.

As John Robbins says, we all know people who eat well and get sick. We all know people who eat junk and thrive. But we have far better odds for healthy lives and vibrant bodies when we eat more consciously and make healthier choices. It is UP TO US TO BE RESPONSIBLE FOR OUR OWN GOOD HEALTH. I would highly recommend this book to add to your knowledge if you are looking to become a more healthy consumer of foods.

In the end, my being vegan doesn't mean I am deprived. It doesn't have to mean that for you either. Quite the contrary, my meals are often quite delectable and leave me happy and content. In fact, I eat better and healthier now than I did before I changed my entire way of eating. I wasn't a junk food eater, but I did eliminate a whole host of fruits and vegetables in an effort to maintain a decent weight. Now, I eat more of everything and better in a healthy way and still control my weight.

Adding more fruits and vegetables and foods in their whole states to your diet is a good thing. However, if that's all you do, it won't be quite enough. Dr. McDougall says doing it 100% will cause huge, beneficial changes that 90 or 95% won't.

If you think you can't do this, think again. Give it a good try for at least 30 days. See what it does for your health and the way you feel, then reassess the situation.

Mom

In A Nutshell

- Ideally, eat NO animal products. They are loaded with fat and cholesterol. Unquestionably, the Standard American Diet is comprised of way more protein than our bodies need. We are actually CAUSING osteoporosis by consuming too much protein as it leaches the calcium from our bones. Please be aware of this.
- Incorporate more beans and oats into your meals. They are high in fiber and will lower your cholesterol. Raw almonds and walnuts also lower cholesterol and give you the much needed Omega 3s, but eat these sparingly if you are trying to lose weight.
- Eat copious amounts of fresh fruits and vegetables, not only for snacks, but also for meals, throughout the day and whenever you get a hunger attack.
- Lemon water - Squeeze the juice of half a lemon into 10 ounces of filtered water. It's a great cleanser and it alkalizes. And remember, disease does not exist in an alkaline body. Animal foods are highly acidic.
- Comprise your daily diet of MOSTLY Raw Foods. It's where you'll get most-needed enzymes, as they are LOST in cooked foods.
- Eliminate all together, if you can, white flour, white rice, refined sugar, table salt, packaged foods, and junk foods of any kind.
- Minimize greatly your oil intake. Steam in water rather than sauté in oil.
- Supplement your diet with omega 3 rich foods such as: flaxseed, hemp seed, walnuts and dark leafy greens.

Here it is: It's your choice, ultimately. Do your own research. There are a plethora of books and studies to prove this point. Look for the truth about diet and how it is related to disease. Be responsible for your own health and do not be fed blindly what the mainstream feeds you. Do not be led as lambs to the slaughterhouse! Take heart. Have the courage to separate yourself from the flock who does follow blindly. Don't be fooled and don't be swayed by corporate greed.

Part Two

Recipes for, not only Your Enjoyment but also, your good health

Recipes

Appetizers

Guacamole

6 - 8 not-green-not-ripe-but-just-right-avocados just ever so soft to the touch. Too soft and they're not good. Too hard and they're not good either. There is only a very short window of time, like bananas, with avocados, so you have to get them JUST RIGHT. If, by chance, you can't find just-right avocados, buy them green and place them in a brown bag for a day or so. They will be just-right the next day or so. Double this recipe for more.

Juice of two lemons

1 bunch cilantro, chopped fine

1 bunch green onions, sliced thin

2 fresh tomatoes, diced

Sea Salt & Pepper to taste

Slice the avocados around lengthwise. Twist to pull apart. Take the part of the knife blade toward the handle and give a whack to the pit with it. Twist slightly to pull the pit out and discard. Or, you could root it to grow an avocado tree. They're not all fertile, but when you do find a fertile one, it will root.

Holding half of the avocado in the palm of your hand and with the point of your knife, slice into the halves of the avocado (just to the skin, not all the way through) length-wise and width-wise to form little squares. (Demonstration video on my website to show how to do this; sometimes you just have to see things done).

When you have the little squares cut up within the shell, take a spoon and scoop them out onto a flat plate. Now, with a large fork, mash a few avocados at a time, not so they are mushy, just coarsley-lumpy. When mashed, transfer to a bowl and pour the fresh lemon juice over all to keep from browning. Mix with two spoons to incorporate.

Chop the onions, cilantro and tomatoes and add to the guacamole. Add sea salt and pepper to taste and serve with chips. You can top chili with it, put it in a wrap or eat it just as is. Yum!

I usually put this in two bowls and use one at a time. Cut parchment paper the size of the inside of your bowl and press lightly onto guacamole mixture. Then cover bowl very tightly with saran wrap. Guacamole browns very rapidly, so I take this care to keep it from browning too quickly. If by chance you don't use it all, then your second bowl is still intact. Some people put the pits into the guacamole to keep from getting brown.

P. S. To save a bit of time, you could mix all the avocados in your food processor but I don't like the completely smooth texture. A few lumps makes it more appealing. At least in my view.

Serves a Crowd

Just a few years ago, I had no idea what to do with an avocado, much less make guacamole. Our daughter Mary Carol's friend, from California, was quite familiar with it and taught me how to make it. It's the best! Just one small change. He uses lime juice; I use lemon juice (Please see video on my website for demonstration of how to cut an avocado and how to make guacamole).

www.Carobi5.com

Artichoke Spread

Excellent! *This one's a winner*

1/2 cup raw almonds, coarsely chopped

2 to 3 cloves garlic, minced

1 (14-ounce) can artichoke hearts, drained and chopped finely

1 small Vidalia (if in season) or sweet onion, minced

1/2 to 3/4 cup vegan mayonnaise

Juice of one small lemon

Fresh dill, about 2 tablespoons snipped

Fresh parsley, about 2 tablespoons snipped

Mix all ingredients together. Season with salt and pepper. Let sit in refrigerator for several hours for flavors to meld. Can and should be made ahead. Serve with your favorite crackers.

Artichokes Italian-Style a la Connie

These are a real delicacy. My mother made them so often they were a staple in our house when I was growing up. However, I did not appreciate them then.

2 - 3 Artichokes

1 cup Bread crumbs

1 teaspoon Oregano

Garlic powder

Salt & Pepper

Fresh Mint chopped, about 2 tablespoons

Oil

Cut bottom off artichokes. Trim all leaves. Rinse and spread leaves apart.

Mix all ingredients together and stuff mixture into each section.

Fill a pan with about 1 - 2 inches of water. Add the juice of 2 Lemons to the water.

Gently place stuffed artichokes into pan. Drizzle oil over artichokes.

Start on high and just before it starts to boil, turn to simmer for 30 - 45 minutes. When leaves are tender and pull away easily, they are done. ***Yum!***

Take each leaf and scrape the bread crumb mixture and the meat of the artichoke leaf with your bottom teeth.

> *After all the trouble you go to, you get about as much actual "food" out of eating an artichoke as you would from licking 30 or 40 postage stamps.*
> *—Miss Piggy*

A Colorful Pepper-Corn-and-Bean-Dip

Excellent!

1 each red, green and yellow pepper

1 small onion

1 jalapeño pepper

1 small jar pimento

1 package frozen corn

1 can pinto beans

1 can black beans

Chop peppers, pimento and onion very fine. Add rest of ingredients. Pour cooked dressing over all and stir well.

Dressing

Boil 3 to 4 minutes

1/2 cup Agave Sweetener

1/2 cup vinegar

1/3 cup oil

Cool and pour over vegetable mixture. Serve with your choice of chips or crackers.

Pine Nut Pesto

1 cup pine nuts

1 bunch of fresh basil

3 tablespoons olive oil or enough to moisten

2 garlic cloves

A sprinkle of salt

Mix well in a food processor. Serve with toasted baguettes or your favorite crackers.

Red Bell Pepper Spread

Thank you, Charlotte. Delicious! Everyone clamors over this one.

2 red peppers, chopped

2 (14-ounce) jars roasted red bell peppers, drained and coarsely chopped (optional)

1 cup Kalamata olives, pitted and chopped

Any amount or combination of: Rosemary, oregano, basil, and/or thyme, chopped fine.

2 tablespoons olive oil

2 tablespoons balsamic vinegar

Fresh ground pepper

Serve with small rounds or squares of bread or crackers.

To satisfy the cheese eaters, you might want to spread the bread with goat cheese first if you so desire.

Marvelous Marinated Mushrooms

Buy fresh mushrooms, cut a bit off the stem end so there is a clean bottom and marinate in a zesty Italian salad dressing. Let sit for two days in refrigerator for flavors to meld. Put mushrooms on a decorative plate with food picks and you have a quick and easy appetizer. Excellent flavor.

Eggplant and Zucchini Bruschetta

3 heads of garlic, roasted

1 medium eggplant, diced small

1 zucchini, diced small

1 medium tomato, diced small

1 teaspoon sea salt

2 teaspoons Italian seasoning

2 teaspoons oregano

Several fresh basil leaves, minced

Bread slices of your choice

Sauté eggplant and zucchini in a fry pan with a bit of water until tender and done.

Add the tomato to the skillet, stir the mixture until done. Add rest of ingredients. Stir for 2 minutes or so until everything is well incorporated. Set mixture aside.

Line a cookie sheet with all the bread slices. Lightly brush each slice with olive oil, then toast in a 325° oven for 3 or 4 minutes until ever so slightly toasted. If you don't like it crunchy, watch carefully.

Remove bread slices from oven and spread with garlic sauté mixture.

Arrange on a platter and serve.

Sometimes I will toast any sliced bread I have on hand and cut it into quarters. It's just as good as French Bread or Baguettes.

Talking About Food

One night Bill and I were out to dinner in Orlando with our friends. I don't recall now what we all ordered but the three of us were ooohhing and aaahhing with each forkful to our mouths. We were simply relishing every bite and morsel of food on our plates. I say the three of us because as I've mentioned, Bill only eats to live. Between him and our Daniel, they feel it's an imposition to have to stop what they are doing to eat because they are hungry. Being Italian, I have no earthly comprehension of this. Bill sat there and added not one comment unless the subject veered from food. Later, he said to me, "That was the most boring part of the evening, when you were all talking about food!" We've laughed over this many times how some of us can enjoy food so much and others, not at all.

Traditional Tomato Bruschetta

2 - 3 tomatoes, diced small

2 - 3 garlic cloves, diced small

Lots of fresh basil, cut up

Drizzle of oil and sea salt and pepper

Mix all ingredients together.

Follow directions on Eggplant and Zucchini Bruschetta. Brush bread slices with a bit of olive oil. Toast in a 325° oven. Top with tomato mixture and enjoy.

Marinated Green Olive Nibbles

For a striking presentation, double or triple the recipe and turn into a large clear bowl or compote. Looks lovely not to mention the great taste.

1 (16-ounce) can large, pitted, green olives

4 stalks celery with leaves, cut into 1-inch pieces

3/4 cup oil

3/4 cup red wine vinegar

4 garlic cloves, finely minced

1 teaspoon pepper

3/4 teaspoon red pepper flakes

1 tablespoon oregano

Drain olives and place in a large bowl along with the celery. Mix remaining ingredients together and pour over olives and celery, mixing to coat well. Cover and refrigerate over night.

Kale Chips

Wash a bunch of Kale. Pat dry but not completely dry. Cut up into bite size pieces. Place in a bowl and sprinkle with a bit of sea salt.

Place onto a cookie sheet and bake at 350° for 10 - 15 minutes or until crispy.

Now, you know how most of my family eats? They don't like anything green and EVERYONE loves these.

It's a great snack that's also healthy. Gives you the salty and the crunch and the nutrients all at the same time. How much better than that does it get? Serve these alongside a wrap for lunch.

In the islands one of our favorite places to go, and dining out one evening with two other couples, friends of ours, we were at the lovely Caicos Cafe. You know everything is pretty much open-air in the islands. So I meandered toward the kitchen and asked Perik if he would do a vegan dish for me. He had told me previously he would. Of course, no problem. I gave him the parameters and when his son, J brought it out, he said, "This turned out so great, we've decided to offer it as a "special" tomorrow night." How's that for service? It was fried rice with lots of veggies in it, two skewers of baby green and yellow zucchini, sliced thin and three thin dollar sized slices of eggplant. Indeed, the flavor was exquisite, a pleasure for my palate!

Salads

Green-Beans-Tomatoes-and-Lots-of-Wonderful-Basil-Salad

2 cups fresh green beans, cooked and drained, or frozen if you don't have fresh

Lots of fresh basil, chopped

6 fresh, firm, red tomatoes, diced

Freshly ground pepper

1 package of Zesty Italian Salad Dressing

Mix all ingredients together. Refrigerate. Serve on lettuce leaves if desired, or as a side.

Orange-Broccoli-Carrot-and-Raisin-Salad

The orange lends a lovely flavor to this dish.

1 bunch of fresh broccoli florets, broken into very tiny pieces

1 package or several carrots, shredded

1/4 cup raisins, soaked for a couple of hours to plump up

1/4 cup sunflower seeds

3/4 cup orange juice

1/2 cup Veganaise or enough to moisten

2 Tablespoons Agave sweetener or more to taste

Mix all ingredients together and enjoy

Salt to taste

Whisk the orange juice and veganaise together until smooth. Mix with rest of ingredients until well incorporated. Enjoy!

Variation: Skip the orange juice and veganaise add a drizzle of oil and red wine vinegar, instead.

Salad Tip: For beautifully, crisp greens, do this: Early in the day, wash salad greens. Drain well. Wet a large, clean dish towel and squeeze until all water is out. Wrap the salad greens tightly in this wet towel and place in the salad bowl you will be using for the completed salad. Refrigerate for several hours. When ready to serve, unwrap the towel and place the greens in the bowl. Add tomatoes, carrots, celery, cucumbers and whatever else you desire plus dressing of your choice. Our favorite is olive oil, red wine vinegar, onion powder, salt and pepper. Toss all together and serve. Salad is cold and very crisp.

Crunch-Salad with-Black-Eyed Peas

Excellent! Black-Eyed Pea Salad

2 (14-ounce) cans black-eyed peas, rinsed and drained

1 each green, red and yellow peppers, chopped

1/2 red onion, chopped

1 jalapeño pepper

1 avocado, chopped

2 tablespoons lemon juice

2 cloves garlic, minced

1/4 cup olive oil or less (I usually just drizzle a little over the salad)

Red wine vinegar (I also just drizzle a little vinegar over the salad as well, to taste)

A couple squirts of Agave nectar

Sea Salt & Pepper, to taste

2 or 3 fresh tomatoes, diced

1 bunch green onions, chopped

A handful of sunflower seed sprouts, maybe a cup or so.

Cut up avocado and toss with lemon juice to prevent from turning brown. Mix rest of ingredients. Toss well. Refrigerate and serve cold.

Serves 8 - 10

You can even put this salad on a tortilla and eat as a wrap. My girls request this one a lot.

Peas, Shoe Peg Corn and Green Bean Salad

Another crunchy, fresh, nutritious dish to have you coming back for more.

1 can shoe peg corn or frozen if available. If you can't find organic shoe peg corn, use regular corn.

1 package frozen young sweet peas

1 package frozen green beans

1 cup celery, diced

1 medium sweet onion, diced

1 bunch green onions, sliced

1 green Pepper, diced

1 jar Pimento, diced

Several drizzles of Agave nectar to sweeten

Drizzle Vinegar & Oil to taste.

Salt & Pepper to taste

Mix all ingredients together.

Serves 8 - 10

Wild Rice Pilaf

Several of these salads used in conjunction with each other make a lovely and full meal, for either lunch or dinner.

2 cups cooked Wild Rice

1 cup cooked Brown Rice

1/2 cup walnuts

2 Baked and cubed sweet potatoes

1/3 cup dried cranberries

1/2 cup celery, sliced

1 cup shredded carrots

1 bunch green onions

1/2 cup pecan pieces

Sea Salt to taste

A drizzle of olive oil

Mix all ingredients together and enjoy as a side or as an entree lunch salad.

Serves 6 - 8

Mung Bean Salad

This recipe, along with her comments, is from a friend of mine.

Hi Carol, Here is the mung bean salad recipe. It is one of my favorites...... very nutritious, inexpensive to make, colorful to look at and yummy! Love, Barb

2 cups unsprouted mung beans (makes about 5-6 cups when sprouted)

1/2 cup celery, minced

1 bunch scallions, chopped

1 red pepper, chopped

Juice of 1 lemon

2 tablespoons olive oil

1-2 tablespoons fermented soy sauce

Pinch of cayenne powder

Mix all ingredients and marinate for at least 1 hr.

Sprouting Mung Beans: Soak beans in water for 8 hours; drain in fine strainer in sink; rinse 3-4 times /day. They will be ready in about 2-3 days.

Serves 6 - 8

I received this e-mail from my daughter, Keri, last night, parentheses mine.

Mom,

I forgot to tell you that Kerigan (she's 7) got stuck in our tree out in front on Sunday.

I sent Kennedy (her older 12 year old sister) out to call her in to get ready for dinner and she came back in telling me that she was in the tree and couldn't get out. Now, this was a little like her speaking French to me. So, I went out to see 6 neighborhood girls all standing around the tree peering up. As I got closer, I saw my little one who looked like a monkey...hanging on for dear life and not taking the advice from anyone.

So...as this was no time for: I dunno how! Or, I can't or How do you? Or can you? Or I won't...I had to run in the house, grab my tennis shoes, grab the ladder (that I can barely carry), and banged everything on my way out to the tree.

Had to position it just right and willing to take the fall if needed, I started the climb. Dawned on me that if I wanted her out, I had to go up and get her myself.

As I looked down to the 6 little ones below holding the ladder for me, I stepped onto one branch and yelled..."JUMP!" She refused!

So, I had to climb higher, with the insurance company on the cell phone just in case!!

One more branch, then another...I am now having flashbacks to my childhood, yet now I am taller and heavier and with back pain still lingering from the birth of this little monkey, it's a little harder to get around, and knowing full well that I haven't been in a tree since I was ten or on a ladder since I was.... we'll, never-mind.

I finally braced myself against a branch and had her fall down into me as I brought her to safety.

So, with that being said, we made it to dinner but there was no time for her shower! Priorities! :-)

Barley-Corn-and-Kidney-Bean-Salad

A lovely, colorful salad full of nutrients

1 cup uncooked whole grain barley
1 frozen package corn
1 (14-ounce) can kidney beans
3 fresh tomatoes, diced
1 each red and yellow pepper, diced
1 bunch green onions, cut up
Several ribs of celery, sliced thin
1 jalapeño pepper, cut up
Bunch of cilantro
2 cloves garlic, minced

Mix all ingredients together and pour dressing over all.

Dressing

The juice of 3 fresh limes
1 t. cumin
Sprinkle of oregano
Tiny bit of salt
A drizzle of oil and vinegar

This is a good make-ahead dish. There is lots of color in it and you can't go wrong with color.

Serves 8 - 10

Tabouli Tabbouleh Taboli Tabouleh Taboule

However you decide to spell it, just include it in your diet as it is rife with nutrition. Bulgur is packed with B vitamins, has fewer calories, is lower in fat and has more fiber than brown rice. It also makes cholesterol less sticky and pulls toxins out of your body. Now, can't you wait to incorporate more of this healthy, whole grain into your diet?

Bulgur along with lentils, green peas, and walnuts are all great sources of essential vitamins for hair loss. [31]

Bulgur was used during World War II for two purposes. One was as a staple to feed the troops and the other was as a sand blasting agent to clean airplane parts. [32]

Bulgur Wheat-Mint-Parsley-and-Cilantro-Salad (AKA Tabouli)

See Image On Page 57.

This wonderfully delicious salad along with a lettuce salad and cooked green beans, broccoli, asparagus or brussel sprouts makes a filling meal.

1 cup bulgur wheat

1 3/4 cups boiling water

The juice of two fresh lemons

3 Red, firm tomatoes, diced

A good firm cucumber, unpeeled and diced

3 - 4 green onions or if you like more, use the whole bunch

1 cup curly parsley and 1 cup cilantro, chopped very fine

A bunch of mint leaves, chopped

1/2 cup cranberries, raisins or currants

1/2 cup pecans chopped

Sea Salt and freshly ground pepper to taste

Pour the boiling water over the bulgur. Stir. Now add lemon juice. Stir again and let sit, about 30 minutes, while you prepare rest of ingredients. Add remaining ingredients to the bulgur and enjoy!

Traditional Middle Eastern tabbouleh is more parsley, less bulgur. The American version is more bulgur, less parsley. Use your own judgment as to proportions.

Serves 4 - 6

You could also have bulgur in place of a processed cereal for breakfast with a little Cinnamon, Agave Sweetener, and Almond Milk.

Wheatberry Salad

Here is another lovely and different lunch dish. It's chewy and filling.

2 cups cooked wheatberries
1 cup shredded carrots
1/3 cup currants
1/2 cup walnut pieces
1 bunch green onions, sliced
3/4 cup fresh parsley, chopped
A drizzle of apple cider vinegar
A drizzle of olive oil
3 Tablespoons Tamari soy sauce
Sea Salt and Pepper to taste

Mix all ingredients together and enjoy!

Serves 6 - 8

Corn and Avocado Salad

I was looking for something to eat for lunch one day and this was what I concocted.

1 Avocado diced

1 package frozen corn

2 fresh tomatoes, diced

1 tablespoon nutritional yeast, optional

1/4 t. red pepper flakes

Sea salt to taste or (kelp). Kelp is a great source of iodine and can be used in place of salt.

Mix all ingredients together and drizzle with a bit of oil and red wine vinegar.

Southwestern Corn Salad

This is similar to what is served in the islands as a condiment with chips and guacamole.

1 (15-ounce) can black eyed peas or black beans, drained and rinsed

1 (11-ounce) can Mexican style corn, drained

1/4 cup finely chopped red onion

1/4 cup fresh cilantro, chopped

1/4 cup olive oil

1/4 cup fresh lime juice

1 teaspoon or more of seeded, finely chopped jalapeno peppers.

Serves 4 - 6

> *I am convinced that good cooking is an art, as well as a form of intense pleasure."*
>
> —*Madame Jahane Benoit*

Cold, Refreshing Asparagus Salad

15 spears Asparagus

Cut into 2-inch pieces. Blanche in boiling water until done just the way you like them. Still a little crisp. Rinse with cold water.

Add:

1/4 cup chopped fresh basil

1/4 cup green onions, sliced thin

1/4 cup cilantro, chopped

Mix well. Combine asparagus and dressing and let marinate for several hours or overnight.

Before serving, add:

1 cup onion, diced

3/4 cup toasted pine nuts

Sea Salt and Pepper to taste

Dressing

Wisk together:

4 Tablespoons fresh lemon juice

2 Tablespoons Dijon Mustard

4 Tablespoons extra virgin olive oil

Serves 4 - 6

Everything-But-the-Kitchen-Sink-Salad

I start with the large box of the organic spring mix from Costco. Sometimes I add chopped romaine or baby spinach to the salad mix.

Then I add small grape tomatoes, hearts of palm, artichoke hearts, pine nuts, craisins (or any dried fruit mix I have around), sometimes I add sweet onion slices, yellow, red and orange peppers; sun dried tomatoes and either feta or Parmesano Reggiano cheese. Green peppers and I don't get along, and I'm not a walnut or pecan person, however, you could put them in if you like. Mandarin oranges and strawberries work well too. Sometimes I add a little fresh mint as a teaser.

For the dressing I use various ones, usually bottled:

Greek Vinaigrette

Caesar Vinaigrette

Balsamic Vinaigrette - various kinds

Raspberry Vinaigrette

Sometimes I make one using Nakano seasoned rice vinegar, spanish olive oil and spices.

I dress it very lightly and mix everything really well (with my hands and plastic gloves), then I add a little more dressing and lightly toss it again.

You can use 2 different dressings when you do this as well. Start with a poppyseed and then go to a fruit vinaigrette as the second - something I learned from Pat (another friend of ours).

The bowl I have been using lately is a large ice bucket and I love that you can see the salad. Hope this is helpful; I love a salad that has lots of stuff in it.

So do I, Barb. Thank you. This bowl she speaks of is very narrow and tall and makes a striking presentation for the salad. This is truly a wonderful salad. I told her that I sometimes add green and black and/or Greek olives to my salads, too. So, if you have to take a dish to a party or potluck, this one works quite well.

Serves 10 - 12

At many gatherings where a group of us bring food, this salad stands out as awesome. I thought I made a good salad, but this one wins hands down. When I emailed my friend, Barb, and asked what made hers so blessed good, this is what she sent me.

I don't think America will have really made it until we have our own salad dressing. Until then we're stuck behind the French, Italians, Russians and Caesarians.

—Pat McNelis

Cabbage Slaw

Thank you, Linda B., for this one. We love it!

1/2 head of cabbage thinly sliced and cut up
2 apples, peels intact , sliced and diced
1/2 cup pecans or walnuts
1/2 cup dried cranberries or raisins
1 tablespoon dijon mustard
1 red onion, finely diced
1 teaspoon fresh lemon juice
1/4 teaspoon cayenne pepper
1 teaspoon freshly ground black pepper

Add:

A drizzle of Agave Sweetner
Salt to taste
Veganaise or vegan mayonnaise, enough to moisten

Mix all ingredients together until well blended

Serves 4 - 6

Mango Slaw

If you like Mango, you will love this dish. It's a favorite of mine served in the Caribbean.

1 cup red cabbage shredded (sliced very thinly)

1 cup white cabbage shredded

1 cup romaine lettuce

1/4 cup cilantro

1 tomato, diced

1 mango, cut-up

Salt and Pepper

Dressing

1 Mango, peeled and diced

1/4 cup white vinegar

1 teaspoon Dijon mustard

2 - 3 tablespoons olive oil

1/4 cup Agave Nectar

Blend and pour over slaw. Mix well.

Serves 6 - 8

> *There is a lot more juice in grapefruit than meets the eye.*
> *—Author Unknown*

Strawberry-Mango Salad

A colorful and healthy dish

1 cup cubed peeled ripe mango, divided

1 T fresh lime juice

1/2 t. vegetable oil

Little orange juice, orange marmalade or Grand Marnier

1/8 t. salt

Salad greens

1/2 cup sliced Fresh strawberries

Mixed nuts, chopped

Put ¾ cup of the mango, lime juice, oil, O.J. and salt into blender or processor until smooth.

Place greens on individual plates. Place remaining mango and strawberries on top of greens. Pour dressing over. Sprinkle with nuts.

Ramen Noodle Slaw Mix

A delicious, always requested, in-place-of-lettuce-salad side.

1 head of cabbage shredded

2 (3-ounce) packages organic vegetable flavored Ramen noodle soup mix

1 cup sliced almonds or pine nuts, toasted

1 cup sunflower kernels

2 bunches green onions, sliced

1/3 cup dried cranberries

3/4 cup oil

1/3 cup agave nectar

1/3 cup white vinegar

Remove flavor packet from noodle packages and set aside. Crush noodles. In a large bowl, assemble all the slaw ingredients.

Combine dressing ingredients: oil, agave, vinegar and contents from the flavor packets. Pour dressing over the slaw and mix well. Cover and chill for several hours or overnight.

Just before serving, add the noodles, toss and serve. For a lighter caloric dish, you could eliminate the noodles. It's just as good without them.

Serves 8 - 10

Gazpacho

My friend, Charlotte, sent this recipe. She is a great cook and we've had many wonderful meals at their house. This is what she says about this wonderful recipe. "*Okay, this is the gazpacho recipe I have perfected over many trial and error years. Tim loves it. I usually use chicken stock, but I substituted veggie stock just for you.*" Thank you, Charlotte.

1 large cucumber, peeled, seeded and diced

2 bunches green onions, chopped

1 large tomato, peeled and diced

3/4 cup salsa (your favorite store bought brand)

2 garlic cloves, minced

1 cup vegetable broth

1 (12-ounce) can V8 Spicy

1 tablespoon fresh lemon juice

2 tablespoons red wine vinegar or balsamic

2 tablespoons Worcestershire Sauce

Tabasco Sauce to taste

2 tablespoons chopped bell pepper

1 finely grated carrot

Salt, pepper, garlic salt, celery salt and cilantro

Blend small batches in blender and mix to desired consistency. Chill. Enjoy!

I've Come A Long Way

Today, many people would say I am a good cook. I entertain frequently and I seem to always be in my kitchen. As the saying goes, "No matter where I serve my guests, it seems they like my kitchen best." And so do I. I have prepared all kinds of wonderful foods: Crown pork roasts, Beef Tenderloins, Beef Wellingtons, Wiener Schnitzel, Chicken a hundred different ways (it was always my favorite meat), an abundance of mouth-watering baked goods: mile high pies, decadent cakes, fancy cream puffs, Cannolis, Italian cookies by the ten dozens, apple strudels, Fudge, Brownies, Tirimisu, cookies of all kinds and more.

Though this was not always the case.

What a mess when, one time many years ago, I had a baked potato explode in my oven. I hadn't pierced it first and left it in too long. No one saw it but me, but I know my face was red.

I also remember, early in our marriage, the time I invited a group of family for a Turkey Dinner. Now, mind you, I didn't have the vaguest idea of how to prepare a turkey. But that was what I chose to make.

My family was out of town and rather than make a long-distance phone call to them, I made a local call to the mother of one of our friends. She kindly gave me her instructions: soak the bird in cold water, wash it well, including the cavity, sprinkle salt on the inside, butter the entire outside, put it in a large roasting pan and roast.

Well, all of this went without a hitch....or so I thought. Came time to carve the turkey and one of my aunts (a perfectionist to say the least) helped at the buffet table. Lo and behold what did she, of all people find? The giblets fully cooked in the paper bag they come in, inside the neck cavity of the bird.

Well, how was I to know? Mrs. V. never mentioned that there were two cavities and the neck was where the butcher stores the giblets. Another time my face was red!

Oh well, I guess you could say I've come a long way since then. A long way since my oven explosion and my first cooked bird!

Entrees

Zucchini Crust Pizza With Lots of Wonderful Toppings

You could add meatless veggie crumbles to this if you want to have a little meaty feel. I'm fine without it, but if you are serving to meat eaters, it might be an option. Though, do keep in mind, these are not considered a health food and soy is one of the ingredients.

3 zucchini shredded or processed in food processor

1 cup whole wheat flour

2 egg replacers

Salt and pepper

Mix all together and spread into bottom of 9 x 13-inch pyrex pan very lightly oiled.

Bake crust at 400° 10 - 15 minutes. Remove from oven and let cool for about 10 minutes.

Top crust with pizza sauce and any of your favorite vegetables:

Spinach, tomatoes, onions, green olives, black olives, broccoli, mushrooms, green peppers, whatever comes to mind and whatever you have on hand.

Bake 400° - 20 minutes or until vegetables are done.

Cut into squares and remove with spatula. It's a little runny, but delicious just the same. If you like cold leftovers as I do, these are much more firm just coming out of the refrigerator.

Serves 12

> ***Do vegetarians eat animal crackers?***
> ***—Author Unknown***

A-Hearty-No-Meat-Chock-Full-of-Vegetables-Good-For-You-Chili

Serves a crowd!

1 medium onion, chopped

1 teaspoon red pepper flakes

2 tablespoons oregano

2 teaspoons garlic powder

1/4 cup chili powder

1 tablespoon cumin

1 tablespoon paprika

1 tablespoon cinnamon

1/3 cup Agave Sweetener

4 tablespoons cocoa powder

4 or 5 ribs celery, chopped

1 green, 1 red and 1 yellow sweet pepper, chopped

2 jalapeño peppers, chopped

3 cloves garlic, finely minced

2 (4-ounce) cans chopped green chilies, drained

3 (28-ounce) cans diced tomatoes (Unless you get petite diced, you may want to dice these into smaller pieces).

1 tablespoon ground black pepper and 1 tablespoon sea salt

1 each (15-ounce) cans kidney beans, garbanzo beans, black beans, all rinsed and drained.

1 package frozen corn

A few fresh basil leaves

Place onion and seasonings in pan with basil, oregano and salt with a bit of water (if you want to eliminate oil all together). Cook and stir until tender. Then, mix in celery, green peppers, jalapeño peppers, garlic and green chili peppers. Simmer for about 5 or 10 minutes until veggies are nearly done.

Reduce heat to low and simmer for another few minutes. Add tomatoes. Season with chili powder, black pepper and red pepper flakes. Add all the beans. Bring to boil, then reduce heat and simmer 45 minutes. At end, stir in corn and cook another few minutes.

Serve over brown rice and top with guacamole and tomato salsa. Add a salad and you have a more than complete meal.

Makes me hungry just writing about it. It's a wonderful dish and I am quite sure you'll go back for seconds.

Just recently, I made a big pot of this chili (it makes a lot). No one in my family was here to eat it but I just felt like it for myself. Well, I could only eat it for so many days, so I began giving bowls of it away to friends. Mind you, these friends are not vegan. But they all came back and said it was delicious and all asked for the recipe. Don't let the list of ingredients deter you, please.

A Poignant Moment

"I was at a party feeling very shy because there were a lot of celebrities around, and I was sitting in a corner alone. A very beautiful young man came up to me and offered me some salted peanuts and he said, 'I wish they were emeralds' as he handed me the peanuts; and that was the end of my heart. I never got it back."

—Actress Helen Hayes before she became a star.

Pasta with Mushrooms and Tomato Sauce

More than hits the mark!

1 pound pasta of your choice

1 pound of fresh mushrooms of your choice

1 teaspoon allspice

3 or 4 bay leaves

1 large onion, diced

4 or 5 garlic cloves

1 (28-ounce) can of tomato sauce

2 cups of red wine

3 cups vegetable broth

2 (28-ounce) cans diced tomatoes

A bunch of fresh basil

Sea Salt & Pepper, to taste

> *I would like to find a stew that will give me heartburn immediately, instead of at three o'clock in the morning.*
> —*John Barrymore*

Sauté mushrooms, allspice, bay leaves, salt and pepper. When mushrooms are brown, add onion and garlic and cook for a few minutes until softened. Add tomato sauce and cook for another few minutes. Add red wine for good flavor. Mix with cooked pasta of your choice. I like Organic brown rice pasta. You can add the basil to the entire dish or set out in a bowl for guests to add their own. ***Yum!***

Split Peas and Pasta

A great one dish meal and with a salad makes a great lunch or dinner.

1 (32-ounce) container vegetarian broth

2 cups water

1 to 2 tablespoons vegetarian base (optional, but it will add more flavor)

1 cup uncooked green split peas. Rinse first.

2 cloves garlic, minced

2 medium onions, chopped fine

1 teaspoon cumin

1 teaspoon cayenne

5 cups chopped Spinach, Kale, Chard, Collard greens or other greens of your choice or a mixture of all three.

1 pound brown rice or whole wheat pasta of your choice: spaghetti, broken into 1″ pieces, elbow mac or penne pasta.

1 bunch fresh parsley or cilantro, chopped

Salt & Pepper

Bring the broth, water and split peas to a boil. Skim. Simmer for 30 minutes. Sauté onions, garlic, cumin and cayenne in a slight bit of water just until soft.

Add to the split peas along with the greens and pasta. Add all other ingredients.

Bring to boil, reduce heat to medium and cook until done.

Add parsley or cilantro at end. Mix well and serve.

Serves 6 - 8

"'Stay! is a charming word in a friend's vocabulary."
—Louisa May Alcott

So is "Come for Dinner."
—Me

Quinoa Paella without the Meat

Lovely! Really Lovely! *Makes lots. Freezes well.*

- 1 onion, minced
- 3 cloves garlic, minced
- 1 1/2 cups quinoa – soaked for a few hours or overnight. Rinse thoroughly to remove bitterness
- 2 t. paprika
- 1/4 t. red pepper flakes
- 1 (28-ounce) can diced tomatoes
- 1 each red and yellow bell pepper, diced
- 1 (14-ounce) can light red kidney beans, rinsed and drained
- 3 cups vegetable broth and 1 – 2 tablespoons vegetable base
- 2 medium zucchini, chopped
- 1 package frozen peas and 1 package frozen corn
- 1 can artichoke hearts, rinsed and quartered

Sauté onion and garlic in water. Add quinoa and cook for about 3 minutes. Add paprika and red pepper flakes, tomatoes, peppers, beans and vegetable broth. Bring to boil. Simmer, covered for 15 minutes.

Add more broth if needed. Add zucchini, peas, corn and artichoke hearts just before serving. Cook a few more minutes until everything is done.

Serves 10 - 12

Red meat is not bad for you. Now blue-green meat, that's bad for you!
—Tommy Smothers

Finding the Time, then Making It!

I have often maintained that we will MAKE the time to do the things we WANT to do. And if we don't WANT to do something, somehow we come up with the excuse that we don't HAVE the time.

I recently spoke with my sister-in-law, Brenda, who works 30 hours a week, is stressed much of the time and who also does not feel well. When I asked how she was feeling she told me that she needs to start taking time for herself. She added, "There is never going to be enough time. There is never going to be enough money and eventually if I wait long enough to do the things I want to do, I'll be too old and sick and won't feel like it. I need to change myself," she added. Wise words, I thought.

I asked what it was that she wanted to do. She said that if all things were equal and everything perfect she would go back to Italy. But what to do right in her own back yard was to read more and work on projects in her own home.

I told her that she was right about there never being enough time. Many people wait for huge chunks of time to get huge projects done and those huge chunks of time rarely come. Thus, the projects don't get completed. Rather, attempt those projects by taking, stealing, borrowing or whatever you have to do to devote an extra 15 minutes a day to reading, studying, or working on that project. If done in a disciplined manner, those 15 minutes add up very quickly to the desired outcome completed.

I, too, have been known to wait for those blocks of time, but I have completed many projects, books included, by doing a little bit everyday or every chance I get.

It's difficult for some of us to sit at home and read for pleasure when we have other things calling to us. In the back of our mind is the fact that we should be working or cleaning or things we feel we must do but not things for pleasure, thus we cannot concentrate at home. Better to maybe go out of the house for a set time each day, to a restaurant or the library. I know I am much better able to concentrate away from my home such as this. Her son, my nephew, has a quiet home in which to study, but he takes himself to the library where the atmosphere is more conducive to studying and reading.

Brenda admitted that probably for the first time in her life she went to a restaurant for lunch all alone which is what she loves and needed. Previously, she had just never thought it important enough to schedule this necessary time as is often the case. She rarely takes time for herself. You go girl!

More she related was about her trip to Cherry, Illinois the day before we had spoken. Her grandfather had died in the Cherry Mine disaster which had occurred on November 13, 1909. Two hundred fifty nine men and boys were killed. It was the impetus that started workman's compensation. That day, there was a dedication ceremony for those who had given their lives in this tragedy where a fire had broken out in the mine. The mine eventually had to be sealed, despite the fact that not all were able to be rescued.

Her grandfather's body wasn't recovered until spring and they only knew who it was by the watch he wore on his decomposed wrist. My sister-in-law has this watch and actually brought it with her to the dedication. People were sharing stories about their loved-ones lost and Brenda was also able to share hers.

She met a woman on this day who had written 80 books and was quite interested in Brenda's story. They became kindred spirits in a way and each was happy to have met the other. If she hadn't attended this dedication, she would have missed a vital life element. She is glad she made the time to go and said it was good for her soul.

Thai Noodles, Creamy and Peanutty

Wonderful! Very Guest worthy!

4 (12-ounce) packages brown rice spaghetti
1 1/2 cups peanut butter, creamy style
1/4 cup rice vinegar
1/4 cup chili sauce
1 1/2 cups Agave Sweetener
1 cup soy sauce
1 teaspoon sesame oil
2 bunches green onions, sliced thin
2 cloves garlic, minced
1 tablespoon ginger
2 – 3 cups shredded carrots
1 cup parsley, finely minced
1/2 to 3/4 cup peanuts, chopped

Cook spaghetti in salted, boiling water. Drain but not completely so as not to stick together.

Combine peanut butter, rice vinegar, chili sauce, soy sauce, Agave, and sesame oil in a bowl. Using a wire whisk, mix until smooth. Set aside.

Sauté onions and garlic in a bit of water. Add sauce and heat through. Now, drain the rest of the noodles. Pour sauce over noodles and toss being sure to incorporate well. Add carrots, parsley and peanuts. Toss again.

You can make this early in the day for serving that evening. It's great because it can be served warm or is just as good at room temperature.

Serves 10 - 12

This is one of Mary McDougall's recipes. As a fairly new vegan and before I had a repertoire of my own vegan recipes, I called Dr. McDougall's office one day desperate for a vegan recipe for guests. Carol McDougall told me that everyone who tries this one loves it. I changed the title and adapted it by changing a couple of the ingredients. Thank you, McDougalls. You were right, Carol; it's delicious.

> *Chemicals, n: Noxious substances from which modern foods are made.*
>
> *—Author Unknown*

Pakoras

A Pakistani dish

2 cups Besin flour (Chickpea flour found in an Indian market), or you could grind your own chickpeas into flour if you are so inclined.

1 teaspoon salt

1 teaspoon red chilies (powder)

1/2 teaspoon baking powder

1 1/2 cups water (not all at once)

4 medium onions, sliced thin

3 medium potatoes, sliced thin

1 bunch of mint leaves, chopped

1 tablespoon cumin seeds

In bowl, mix flour, a bit of water at a time, salt and red chilies. Add potatoes and onions to mixture. Add mint and baking powder. Mix well. Add cumin seeds and mix again. Add water as needed to form a rather thick consistency.

Heal oil in a large fry pan. Bring to sizzling. Scoop mixture with 1/4 cup measuring cup. Form each 1/4 cup of mixture into a ball, then flatten in your hand and place in oil. Sauté until golden brown and drain on paper towels.

Top with green Salsa Verde mixture (p. 77) or your own favorite hot sauce.

You can also add other veggies such as cauliflower, eggplant, or whatever veggies you might have on hand.

Serves 6 - 8

My friend Maria makes these for us, They are different and are really very delicious!

The cook is a hand-craftsman, very much like a smith or a potter.

—Nicholas Freeling

Curried Chickpea Croquettes with Salsa Verde

Top with the Mint Salsa Verde, recipe on page 77. Decidedly different!

2 (15-ounce) cans chick peas, rinsed. Or, if you prefer to cook fresh, use those.

1 cup parsley, chopped

2 cloves garlic, chopped fine

1/2 teaspoon cumin

3/4 teaspoon curry powder

Salt and Pepper

2 tablespoons whole wheat flour

In a food processor, pulse the chickpeas, parsley, garlic, cumin, curry, and salt & pepper until well blended. Do not over-mix. Mixture should clump together when squeezed a bit. Take about ¼ cup of mixture and form into patties. Coat with scant sprinkle of flour.

Heat oil in a large fry pan or griddle (Do not crowd together as they will be difficult to turn). Sauté croquettes until golden, just a few minutes per side, gently flipping until done. Watch carefully so they don't burn.

Spoon salsa verde on top (p. 77).

Serves 4 - 6

> *It would be nice if the Food and Drug Administration stopped issuing warnings about toxic substances and just gave me the names of one or two things still safe to eat.*
>
> —*Robert Fuoss*

Salsa Verde

1 1/2 cups parsley, chopped
3/4 cup fresh basil (or ¾ ounce package of basil)
3/4 cup fresh mint (or ¾ ounce package of mint)
1 (2.4-ounce) jar of capers, rinsed
4 cloves garlic, minced
Scant ¼ cup olive oil
4 tablespoons red wine vinegar
1 tablespoon Dijon mustard
1 tablespoon Prepared mustard.
Sprinkle of coarse salt.
1/4 cup pine nuts, coarsely chopped

In food processor, blend all ingredients until smooth. Add coarsely chopped pine nuts. Mix well and serve.

Serves 4 - 6

Called chutney by the Columbians, this sauce is wonderful on the Chickpea croquettes on previous page or the Pakoras on page 75.
It's even lovely on roasted potatoes. It will keep in the refrigerator a week or more.

A New Pass Time:

I am sitting on the beach one day and the children are playing. I cringe as Sabastian, Akia and Kerigan start high on the beach and roll over and over and over again (as we used to do down hills of grass), until they reach the sea. Covered from neck to toe in sand, they roll and splash into the water rinsing off all the sand. Refreshing! And they do this at least a dozen times before they tire of it and move on to something else. I smile as I watch them.

Beans and Rice

A nutritious and hearty bean meal. My friend, Fabiola, makes this for us and it is oh so "delectable" as my Dad used to say!

1 package (15-mixed) beans, dried

3 bay leaves

1 teaspoon garlic powder

1 teaspoon lemon pepper

1 teaspoon Adobo Goya seasoning with cilantro

Salt and Pepper to taste

1 bunch fresh cilantro, finely chopped

Soak beans overnight. Fill a large pot with enough water to cover the beans. Next morning, rinse the beans and change the water, again, putting enough water in pot to cover the beans. Let come to boil. When beans are nearly cooked, about 1 ½ hours, add all the spices and flavorings. Continue cooking on simmer until done. At end, top beans with cilantro and cover, until ready to serve.

Spoon over cooked, brown rice and top with homemade salsa (below).

Fabiola also makes the best salsa. Only thing is every time she makes it, it's different. Sometimes more tomatoes. Sometimes more parsley. Sometimes more cilantro. Whichever way she decides to create this dish, it is always, bar none, always delicious.

Tomato Salsa

This is the best! I can't stop eating it. Serve over beans and rice, or enchiladas or chili or over guacamole or spread down a wrap. It's good on practically anything.

1 bunch cilantro, finely chopped

2 onions, diced

2 fresh tomatoes, chopped

1 bunch green onions

2 (28-ounce) cans small diced tomatoes, drained very well

Juice of 4 limes. Quarter these and squeeze.

Salt and Pepper to taste

A drizzle of olive oil

Mix all ingredients together and enjoy!

How to Cook for Non-Vegan Friends and Family

After my transition to the vegan world, cooking became a little confusing and frustrating for me. After all, I was the only one eating vegan. I still hosted all the holidays and other special meals for our children and didn't want to make the traditional foods I'd been used to cooking. But then, they didn't want to eat vegan either, so here we had a dilemma.

Further, how could I invite people to dinner when they were used to my traditional meals and now I was no longer cooking them? I would say most people are polite and would eat the food if that's all there was and not complain about it.

Things were different with my own family. Bill hates vegetables and needs and wants his meat. It was all foreign to our adult children, as well, and they've had a difficult time with this change, though I must say that they've been good sports about it. They even accommodate me with meatless meals when we are invited to their homes for dinner.

Some of Bill's cousins were in town one weekend and I invited them to dinner. Eight siblings, their spouses and our own immediate family; the group numbered more than twenty. They're Irish and they like my Italian Spaghetti, but it's all I've ever made for them. I wanted a change. Besides, I wasn't going to cook the sauce with meat, so now what do I do? Though none of them are vegan, I decided to make a completely vegan meal. Hearty eaters, they were sure to like it, I thought. I took the chance. I prepared about ten different dishes and the buffet table was laden.

It's always a compliment to me when people go back for seconds and many of them did that day. It was food they were not used to much less aware of. Yet, they liked it. A big change and a success, nonetheless.

Because I am the only one in our family, I don't push. I still make the traditional turkey for Thanksgiving and I will have a meat or seafood for Christmas for them, along with many vegan side-dishes for me. Everyone else is satisfied and I haven't compromised my own conviction. They have gotten an introduction to all the vegan side-dishes and they've found many they like and even request, mind you! It's still a work-in-progress and I continue to search for ways to satisfy them with healthier foods.

As a child my family's menu consisted of two choices: take it or leave it.
—Buddy Hackett

> **A Word About Peas**........*the impatience to eat them, the pleasures of having eaten them, the joy of having eaten them again, are the three questions which have occupied our princes for the last four days. There are ladies who, having supped with the King, go home and there eat a dish of green peas before going to bed. It is both a fashion and a madness!*
> *—Madame de Maintenon, a lady to the court of Louis XIV*

Peas and Macaroni

1 large onion, diced

2 (15-ounce) cans stewed tomatoes, blended

1 (28-ounce) can diced tomatoes

1 package frozen peas

1 pound of elbow macaroni

Salt and lots of Black Pepper to taste

I don't usually season with a whole lot of pepper, but for some reason I load it on in this dish. Makes for wonderful flavor.

Sauté onion in a bit of oil or water in a Dutch oven. Add a good bit of water, maybe 6 cups, tomatoes and onions. Let cook for 1 hour until flavors meld. Add the peas, then add the pasta. Cook until done. Season with salt and pepper.

Serves 6 - 8

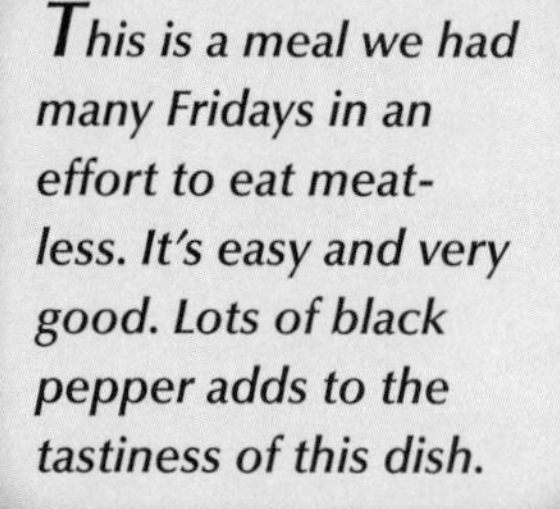

Bean and Corn Casserole

2 (28-ounce) cans chunky tomato sauce
1 onion, diced
1 bunch green onions, sliced thin
1 tablespoon cumin
1 tablespoon paprika
1 (15-ounce) can black beans, rinsed and drained
1 (15-ounce) can White Cannellini beans, rinsed and drained
2 (15-ounce) cans Pinto beans
1 package frozen corn
1 (5.75-ounce) can sliced, pitted black olives
1 large bag corn chips, crumbled
Sea salt to taste

Layer in a 9 x 13 inch pan: chunky tomato sauce, onions, cumin, paprika, beans, and corn. Repeat layers. Top with remaining sauce or diced tomatoes and diced olives.

Bake 350° 25 - 30 minutes. Served topped with crumbled tortilla chips. This can also be served over cooked brown rice or stuffed into a baked potato.

Serves 6 - 8

First time I made this, I even ate it cold the next day. Put it on a Spelt Tortilla with avocado and sprouts and rolled it into a wrap. Yum! You can even top this with homemade salsa. My son, William, likes hot and he said that a couple of added jalapeño peppers would kick it up a notch!

If organic farming is the natural way, shouldn't organic produce just be called "produce" and make the pesticide-laden stuff take the burden of an adjective?

—Ymber Delecto

Bill was going through some papers the other day and found this note he left for our youngest child (some 24 years ago), Mary Carol, who was 6 at the time. We lived in Wisconsin on a lake. It was hurriedly scribbled, before he went off to work, on the back of a restaurant check. Pretty typical of him, his thoughts and his writings. Made us all smile then and even now again all these years later.

Dear Mary Carol, Be nice to William, help your mom, miss me. empty the lake, wash the trees, mow the roof and don't forget to put the wind in a bottle.

Love you, Dad

Italian Pasta Sauce

Into a large pot (one with enough boiling space), add:

2 (15-ounce) cans tomato sauce

2 (10 to15-ounce) cans tomato paste

1 1/2 cans of water to each can of paste and each can of sauce. It will be fairly thin. Turn heat to high and let come to a full rolling boil. If you want to add less water, it will lessen the cooking time and still be just as good.

After it comes to a boil, add:

2 teaspoons basil

2 teaspoons Italian seasoning

2 teaspoons oregano

2 - 3 bay leaves and a bunch of fresh basil

1/2 to 3/4 cups of sugar (I now add 1/2 cup of Agave sweetener instead). You can't tell the difference and the Agave has less of an impact on the glycemic index. Now you might think this is too much sugar but we Sicilians like it sweet. Besides, it takes the tartness out of the tomatoes.

Then, add Salt and Pepper to taste. Lots of pepper gives it a good flavor. After you've added all the seasonings, turn the heat down and let simmer for 2 or 3 hours or until it is thickened to your liking, but not too thick. This must be stirred often being sure to scrape the bottom of the pan so it doesn't burn. Once you have burned the bottom, you will be sure to stir often, so be ever vigilant.

Cook 1 pound of your favorite pasta in boiling, salted water. Drain pasta very well. Put back into cooking pot, then ladle several cups of sauce onto the pasta until it is well saturated. Incorporate sauce into pasta. Put pasta into a decorative bowl and serve with more sauce if so desired, a nice salad and garlic bread.

Serves 4 - 6

We call it Sugo and Sundays weren't Sunday without Pasta With Sugo! This spaghetti sauce is one of those old family recipes that has really never been written down. Everyone in my family has always just made it by feel. I have since taken the meat out of it and we all still think it's pretty good.

Nutty-Couscous-with-Mint-and-Tomatoes

1 (10-ounce) box Couscous, cooked according to package directions.

8 - 10 radishes, very finely chopped

1 bunch green onions, very finely chopped

1/4 cup currants

1/2 cup fresh parsley, very finely snipped

1/4 cup fresh mint leaves, very finely chopped

2 medium tomatoes, very finely chopped

1/2 cup pine nuts, toasted

Mix the above ingredients together with the cooked Couscous.

Toss with a light vinaigrette dressing.

Taken from my cookbook, Once Upon A Taste Feast, © 2002 - 2009

Vinaigrette Dressing

These amounts are not exact as I usually just drizzle on the oil and vinegar. Less oil, more vinegar is the taste I like, but make it to suit your own taste.

1/2 cup oil

1/4 cup red wine vinegar

Salt & Pepper to taste

Serve at room temperature or heat in oven until just heated through.

Serves 8 - 10

Couscous is a very tiny pasta grain thought to have originated in North Africa, a nice change from rice, and takes nothing at all to cook. It's literally done in a matter of 3 to 5 minutes.
This wonderful dish is served at Houston's Restaurant in Orlando, Florida. They did not divulge their secret to me, but I've scrutinized it quite carefully until I think I've discerned all the ingredients. They use peanuts; I've added pine nuts. In any event, it's a welcome change of pace and quite lovely, indeed.
I think the secret, besides the ingredients themselves, is the fact that everything is "very finely chopped."

Brown Rice with Corn and Peas

- 1 tablespoon olive oil
- 1 cup of cooked brown rice
- 1 cup fresh or frozen corn
- 1 cup fresh or frozen green peas
- 1/2 cup shredded carrots
- 8 green onions, chopped
- 3 cloves garlic
- 1 teaspoon ground cumin
- 3/4 teaspoon oregano
- 1/2 cup tomato sauce
- 3/4 cup water

Add cooked rice, corn, peas, carrots, green onions, garlic, cumin, and oregano in pan with 1 tablespoon oil or a bit of water. Sauté for a few minutes.

Add tomato sauce and water to the rice mixture and combine well. Simmer 15 minutes. Add salt and pepper to taste.

Serves 6 - 8

Rather than white rice, brown rice is ever the more healthy with the bran, germ and the endosperm, the good nutrients, left intact.

Kids!

Last night, my kids and I were sitting in the living room and I said to them, "I never want to live in a vegetative state, dependent on some machine and fluids from a bottle. If that ever happens, just pull the plug."
*They arose, unplugged my computer and threw away my wine. They're such *!!*?**&&!!*

—Author unknown

Brown Rice with Dill and Tomatoes

The dill makes this especially flavorful and pleasant! Another McDougall recipe.

2 cups cooked brown rice

2 cups fresh or frozen corn

1 green pepper, chopped

1 yellow pepper, chopped

8 green onions, chopped

1 fresh tomato, chopped

1 small can black olives, chopped

Fresh chopped dill

Dressing

1 teaspoon Dijon mustard

2 tablespoons water

2 tablespoons red wine vinegar

2 tablespoons soy sauce

Whisk all ingredients together.

Pour over rice salad and mix well. Can be made a day ahead for flavors to mingle

Serves 4 - 6

Spinach with Tomatoes and Potatoes

Thank you Maria for this one we enjoyed together.

1 large potato, any kind, peeled and cut into tiny cubes

A bit of oil

2 cloves garlic, minced

1/2 teaspoon allspice

1/2 teaspoon nutmeg

4 nice red, firm tomatoes, chopped small

1/2 teaspoon chili powder

1 teaspoon ginger

1/2 teaspoon cumin seeds

1 teaspoon ginger, minced

1/2 teaspoon turmeric

Salt to taste

Put about one inch of water in a pan. Add salt and pepper and a little garlic powder. Let come to a boil, add spinach and turn to simmer.

Steam spinach for just a few minutes until it is done. (At this point, I can eat the spinach just like this for a nice lunch dish, drinking the juice and all).

But for the above dish, go ahead and sauté the potatoes in the bit of oil until lightly brown. Remove potatoes and reserve. In the same pan sauté the garlic along with the allspice and nutmeg. Add the spinach, tomatoes, salt, chili powder, ginger and turmeric powder and cook gently for a few minutes. Finally, add potatoes mixing all ingredients together and stir continually. Serve hot with your main meal or with a good bread and salad.

Serves 6 - 8

Spinach is one of those vegetables you either like or you don't. I happen to love it, so if you're like me and like spinach, this is truly a nice dish. I can make an entire meal of it along with a salad.

Collard Wraps

I usually have a couple of wraps and then still have several of the leaves left. These, you can cut up and put in one of your soups.

Or, cut them up and first sauté 1 minced garlic clove in a bit of olive oil. Add the cut up collard greens and stir. Cover and cook over low heat for a few minutes. Then, add 2 tablespoons of walnut pieces and 2 tablespoons of raisins or cranberries. And, there you have a very healthy and nutritious dish for another meal.

For the wrap, wash, dry and cut the thick stem off. Place on a cutting board dark side down, which is the right side.

Spread the leaves with guacamole, hummus, mustard, veganaise or cashew nuts that you've ground in your food processor with 1 tablespoon of lemon juice. This makes a cheese-like spread. Then start filling your wrap, not the entire thing, just a strip down the middle with whatever vegetables you have on hand and whatever are your favorites:

Shredded lettuce

Shredded carrots

Sprouts

Avocado slices

Tomato strips

Celery strips

Green Onions, sliced thin

Red, green and/or yellow pepper strips

Pile it high. Take one end of the wrap and cover your mound of veggies, tucking it in. Then, gently roll to the end. Sort of squeeze it together very gently with your two hands to make it compact. (Check out the video demonstration on my website). **www.Carobi5.com**

You could now cut it on the diagonal in half for a lunch portion or you could cut it on the diagonal into 2″ pinwheels for an appetizer portion. It looks lovely because all the colors are so vibrant. And, though messy to eat, very tasty, indeed. You must try these!

Before I became a vegan, I had only ever heard of Collard greens, much less ever having eaten them. They're about the size of a big ping-pong paddle and come in a bunch. Too much really for the wraps unless you're serving many.

House Art

One day in the 70s a young mother, with three small children in tow, rang my doorbell. When I answered, her question was, would I like to have a pen and ink drawing of my house? WOULD I? Interestingly, I had been thinking of that very thing. I'd seen ads in the backs of magazines for this type of artwork. Here she was at my doorstep. I immediately said yes and was excited at the prospect.

A week later, she presented me with a lovely drawing of my house, matted and ready for framing. I oohed and aahed and absolutely loved it. Although, this artist wasn't aware of her talent, she was humbly surprised when I told her I wanted her to do another of my summer house on the lake. She did this one from a photograph. The detail was exquisite. They were professionally and elegantly done. She could go into business, I thought.

Now, I asked her if she would take a short jaunt to the other side of my small town and sketch a picture of the first house we lived in as newlyweds and new parents. I was totally enthralled with these drawings and for years they have occupied a prominent place in our home. The wall, where the pen and ink drawings hang, tell a story of where we've been. It's a priceless tale that I'm reminded of whenever I look at this gallery.

Taking this one step further, I took one of the drawings to a printer which he copied onto the cover of a fold-over card. I created a poem for the inside and used it for the invitation to a party. At the same time, I also asked the printer to run off some blank copies. Much to my delight, these I used for note cards. We didn't have computers then, so I had to enlist the services of a printer. It would be so much easier today with all of our in-home printing capabilities.

More recently, I had a group of girlfriends over for dinner. One of the girls hadn't been here in awhile and noticed the pen and ink drawings. I explained each home and how the drawings came to be. She was quite taken with the wall of my house-art.

I never kept in contact with the artist, so I don't know if she turned her talent into a business or not. But this young mother with so much talent made me very happy and our house-art evokes lots of conversation.

Adapted from my book: *Embracing Beautiful Moments*

Breakfast Foods

Slightly-Nutty-Non-Dairy-No-Egg-Pancakes

My grandchildren love this vegan version of pancakes.

1 cup whole wheat flour

1/3 cup oat flour

4 tablespoons Agave nectar

2 teaspoons baking powder

1 teaspoon salt

Egg replacer for 1 egg (See page 93 for egg replacers).

1 cup of almond milk

3 tablespoons applesauce

Mix all ingredients together. We like a thicker batter. If you prefer a thinner batter, increase the almond milk slightly.

Lightly coat your griddle with vegan butter before starting the pancakes.

Spread pancakes lightly with vegan butter, your favorite syrup, or what I really love my pancakes topped with is applesauce or canned peaches.

Makes about 10 - 12 Pancakes

Muesli

3 cups rolled oats

3/4 cups raisins or cranberries

3/4 cups chopped walnuts

1/4 cup sesame seeds or pumpkin seeds or both

1 teaspoon cinnamon

Mix all together and store in a covered container in refrigerator. When you are in a hurry and need a quick breakfast, serve with agave sweetener, almond milk and fresh fruit of your choice.

Fruit Smoothie, Delicious and Healthy

This can be made with any fruit you have on hand. Fruit is always a good thing for breakfast. It's what goes through our system the fastest and doesn't lay there for hours or for days as meats and heavier foods do. You can eat this in its whole form or make smoothies from several different types of fruits.

You can usually find me in the kitchen, when all the children are with us for a get-away weekend, blending smoothies for everyone. I pretty much use only fruit and just enough water for it to blend well. Add two or three ice cubes to keep it cold, but that's it. No milk and no powders, but do add sunflower seeds, pumpkin seeds or walnuts both for the nutrition and also to give it a bit of a nutty taste. A good way to incorporate your fruit for the day.

1/2 apple

1/2 orange

2 bananas

1/2 plum

1/2 peach

A few strawberries, blackberries and or raspberries

2 or 3 washed Kale Leaves

1/4 cup of walnuts, sunflower seeds or pumpkin seeds

1 tablespoon flax meal or ground flax seeds

1/2 cup water

Turn blender on high for a minute or two until everything is well blended. Pour into a glass to which you have added a few ice cubes to cool it down.

For a calcium boost, add 2 Kale leaves to your smoothies. If you can get past the unusual green color, you really only taste the fruit. For the good omega 3 fats, add 2 T of Flax meal.

Chia Seed Pudding

Chia Seeds are a wonderfully healthy addition to any diet. I like to eat them for breakfast in the form of a tapioca-like pudding, or for a late night snack. But you can put them in smoothies or sprinkle on salads to get all the nutrients they contain.

They are chock full of anti-oxidants; they contain the healthy omega-3 fatty acids, complete protein, iron and calcium. Chia also contains a full range of B vitamins. Make it a habit to have these on a regular basis as they are so healthy for you. You can order them online or buy them at a health food store.

5 - 6 tablespoons seeds

1 1/2 to 1 3/4 cups Almond milk (depending upon how thick you like it)

1 teaspoon vanilla

1/2 teaspoon cinnamon

A scant 1/3 cup Agave nectar

It will start to thicken pretty quickly. Let sit on counter for a couple of hours and stir every time you walk by it. Give it one last mix and then refrigerate overnight or until it thickens.

Serves 4 - 6

You can make this with Steel Cut Oats. Both are delicious.

Whole Oat Groat Oatmeal

Oatmeal with a nutty chewy, not the starchy, gummy, mushy kind most of us are used to and not, of course, the instant which is fairly void of nutrients. This oatmeal has everything in tact.

If you've never tried whole oat groats, you're missing a treat. These do take awhile to cook (about 45 minutes), but hey! Cook them the night before and have a big bowl in the refrigerator that you can eat from all week. Or, to save time in the morning, measure everything the night before. Put them on the stove as soon as you get up in the morning and while you are getting ready doing other things, they will be cooking. When you are ready for your breakfast, voila! They are done. I always make lots so there is extra on hand. Bill has been known to have a bowl of this at night instead of ice cream. It must be good for that to happen!

For even more healthful benefits, you could just soak these overnight and eat it raw the next morning. Add fruit, non-dairy milk and a bit of cinnamon and walnuts or pecans and you have another great and different dish.

Lemon Water

Lemons are very alkalizing and cleansing. Squeeze the juice of half a lemon into a tall glass of water and sip on it throughout the day.

Various Egg Replacers

1. 1 teaspoon baking powder
1/2 teaspoon baking soda
2 tablespoons flour
3 tablespoons water

Mix together all four ingredients and whisk until foamy (about a minute or so).

Perfect for any recipe that calls for eggs. It is the equivalent of about 2 whole eggs.

2. Or, you could buy Ener G Egg Replacer in a health food store and follow the directions on the box.

3. 1 tablespoon ground Flax seeds and 3 tablespoons water. Stir together until thick.

These are extremely beneficial as they contain the vital omega 3 fatty acids. Incorporate flax seeds in your diet by topping your salads and cereal with them and mixing in with your smoothies. The flaxseed egg replacer is best used in muffins, cookies, or pancakes.

4. 1/2 very ripe banana mashed well is equivalent to one egg. You might only want to use this one if you don't mind the banana flavor in whatever you are making.

Sprouted flour is ever the more healthy than ordinary flour as it digests as a vegetable.

Sides

Roasted Potatoes

A different way with potatoes. Quite nice.

6 - 8 Red and white Idaho Potatoes, mixed, scrubbed clean, with skins intact, and cut into bite size pieces.

Put potatoes in a large bowl and sprinkle liberally with the following:

Garlic powder

Italian Seasoning

Oregano

Basil

Fresh Parsley

Then a good drizzle of olive oil

With two spoons or two clean hands mix everything together until all potatoes are coated. Spread the potatoes in a 9 x 13 inch pyrex pan or a cookie sheet. Bake in preheated 350° oven for about an hour or until tender and very crisp. Actually, the crisper they are the better.

Serves 8 - 10

Broccoli Ala Orange

The orange flavor really enhances the taste of this broccoli dish.

1 Tablespoon vegan butter

1 Tablespoon flour

The zest of two oranges (Chop half and leave the other half in slivers for garnish)

1 large package of frozen broccoli or 1 bunch of fresh broccoli, steamed just until tender.

Melt vegan butter and add flour. Cook for a minute or so, stirring constantly. Add the chopped orange zest. Add the orange juice very gradually continuing to stir until slightly thickened. Pour sauce over cooked broccoli. Garnish with the slivers of orange zest.

Serves 4 - 6

Flat Italian Green Beans and Tomatoes with Greek Seasoning

I knew April wasn't Greek, so I had to know. She adds this little anecdote: I was in my early twenties when I met a very handsome Greek guy from Corfu. I was a pretty decent cook then, but I knew nothing about Greek cooking or food. After dating him for more than 6 years, I picked up a lot and made several of the recipes my own. I even learned how to brew Greek coffee in an Ibriki to perfection. And to this day Greek food is a staple in my home. The handsome Greek guy and I are still friends, although he moved back to Corfu many years ago due to an illness.

April, Thank you for this green bean dish.

1/4 onion, medium diced

1 whole diced tomato

2 cans (or 2 cups fresh) Flat Italian Green Beans

4 tbsp. olive oil

1 small can of unsalted tomato sauce

1/2 - 1 can of water

1/2 teaspoon Uncle Chris Seasoning or Greek Seasoning

Sauté the onions and tomatoes in the olive oil until the onions turn slightly translucent.

Add the tomato sauce and seasoning and stir and simmer for 5 minutes.

Add beans and cook until tender (canned 5 minutes, fresh 15 minutes).

Stir frequently, then enjoy with a loaf of french bread or an entree!!

April says she has made this dish on holidays and alone as the entree when eating light.

It is wonderful with other Greek dishes as well, or served with a rice pilaf.

Serves 4 - 6

We may live without poetry, music and art;
We may live without conscience and live without heart;
We may live without friends; we may live without books;
But civilized man cannot live without cooks.
— Owen Meredith

One Yellow Rose

Discharged from the hospital after a surgery, Bill and I were coming down in the elevator. Bill was cradling a floral arrangement friends had sent him for his birthday while in the hospital. It was a beautiful spring arrangement: snapdragons, carnations, daisies, tulips and one yellow rose.

An older lady stepped onto the elevator and commented on the arrangement, "What a beautiful bouquet of flowers....especially that yellow rose."

With that, Bill plucked the yellow rose from the arrangement, and handed it to her. She couldn't have been more pleased.

Later in the lobby, we noticed that she sat holding it to her heart. As she was departing, she passed us while we waited for a taxi, and said, "That's the first time anyone has given me flowers in ten years.

Then she added, "My husband died ten years ago."

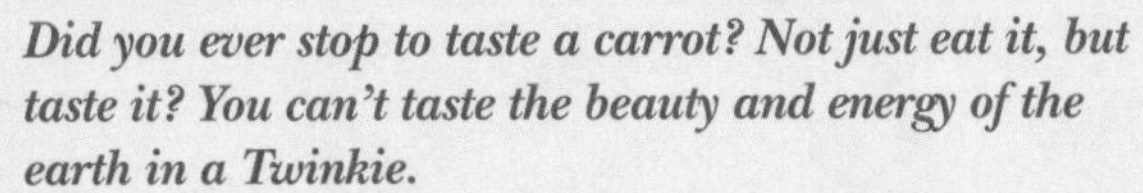

Did you ever stop to taste a carrot? Not just eat it, but taste it? You can't taste the beauty and energy of the earth in a Twinkie.

—Astrid Alauda

Baked Artichoke Hearts with Tomatoes & Onions

Excellent!

2 (14-ounce) cans artichoke hearts, drained and cut-up

1 (28-ounce) can chopped tomatoes, drained

1 bunch green onions, cut-up

1 Tablespoon vegan butter, melted

1 Tablespoon Agave Sweetener

A few fresh basil leaves, cut into strips

Salt and Pepper to taste

Drain artichoke hearts. Sauté green onions in vegan butter until tender. Add artichoke hearts and remaining ingredients. Stir together. Pour mixture into a lightly greased 9 x 13 baking dish. Bake at 325° for about 15 minutes or until heated through.

Serves 10 - 12

There is one thing more exasperating than a wife who can cook and won't, and that's a wife who can't cook and will.

—Robert Frost

My friend, Diana, when she married Jerry 30 years ago told him she couldn't and didn't want to cook. "Me no cook," she said. "Me clean, but me no cook!" So Jerry does it all and she cleans up after him.

Tomatoes Filled with Minted Peas

8 medium tomatoes

2 Tablespoons vegan butter

1 medium onion, minced

1 1/2 teaspoons lemon zest, finely chopped

1 (10-ounce) box frozen baby peas, thawed

Salt & Pepper to taste

4 Tablespoons fresh mint leaves, minced

Melt vegan butter over low heat. Add onion and lemon zest. Cook until tender.

Add peas and season with salt and pepper. Cook for about 5 minutes or until heated through. Stir in mint. Slice 1/4 inch off top of each tomato. Scoop out inside to form a hollow. Invert on paper towels to drain. Spoon pea mixture into tomato shell. Place in shallow baking dish.

Cover with parchment paper and refrigerate overnight. When ready to bake, bring to room temperature before baking. Bake covered at 375° for about 15 minutes or until heated through.

Serves 8

Brown Rice Medley

Do you have leftover rice? If not, make extra for a meal, then refrigerate the rest. For another meal, sauté onion, garlic, shredded cabbage, peas, corn, carrots and celery. Add the refrigerated brown rice to all of the sautéed veggies and you have the equivalent of Chinese fried rice. It is really very good.

The quote below struck a chord with me when I read it. Particularly poignant, I doubt many of us ever give a second thought as to where our rice comes from. Back breaking work, indeed!

Cutting stalks at noontime. Perspiration drips to the earth. Know you that your bowl of rice each grain from hardship comes?

—Chang Chan-Pao

How Hogs Were Raised and Cured

Though this book is about all things vegan, I thought this story of how my aunt Marge's family raised hogs when she was a young girl was interesting. This is what she relates.

"We even raised our own hogs. Every January my father and his brother would butcher two or three. The meat was put down in brine barrels for awhile. After cutting the meat into chops and steaks, it was cooked down, then placed into large, 10 to 20 gallon crocks. The cooked fat on top preserved the meat for the next year as it hardened. The crocks were stored in the basement. The amount of meat needed for meals would be taken out and just reheated or roasted. It was delicious."

Being vegan though, cute, little pigs like this escape the brine barrel.

If we're not willing to settle for junk living, we certainly shouldn't settle for junk food.

—Sally Edwards

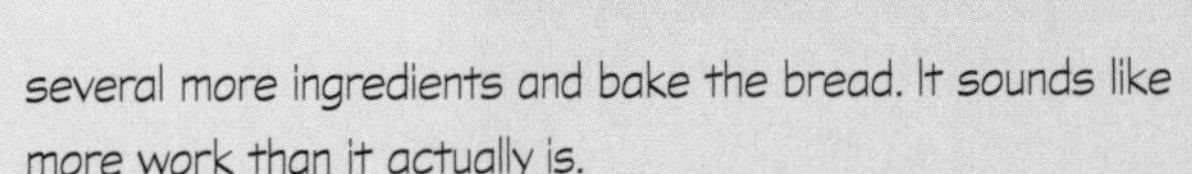

Amish Friendship Bread

Frances Moore and her daughter, Kelly are friends of mine who also write cookbooks. They have a website: www.painlesscooking.com. One of her newsletters talked about baking bread. And this thought came to mind when I read it, so I responded as such:

I have made a few breads over the years but certainly am not an expert at it. I just finished reading your bread page. Very interesting. I remember well, as a child, being told never to slam a door or run through the house when a cake or bread was baking else it would "fall."

How funny now to recall this. I haven't heard it in years.

You are right. Oh the aroma of freshly baked bread, not to mention the fabulous taste. One slice is never enough.

More recently, actually since Valentine's Day, I have been baking Amish Friendship Bread.

My mother made this for YEARS and YEARS. I was given the bread but never the starter. My sister-in-law has also made this for YEARS and YEARS, and again given the bread but never the starter. Why? I have no idea.

After 35 plus years of never having received the starter, my friend, Kit, knocked on my door one day, bless her heart, and gave me the bread AND the starter. I have since made several batches (every 10 days baking) and giving it away. It's been fun.

Fran and I live more than three hours from each other and I told her that I wished we were closer so I could give her and Kelly some bread and starter too because being cooks and bakers themselves, I knew they would not only enjoy it but also appreciate it.

An interesting note about Amish Friendship Bread is that if you give all of your baked bread and all of your starter away, you will have to wait until someone gives you the starter again because the Amish are the only ones who know how to make it. It comes with instructions and you also have to treat it each day by mushing the bag. On the sixth day, you add three ingredients to it and continue to treat it. On the tenth day, you add a few more ingredients to it, then dole out 1 cup measures into four separate baggies - three for friends and one to keep to continue the process. To the remaining batter, you add several more ingredients and bake the bread. It sounds like more work than it actually is.

There are changes upon changes, though, by each one who makes it. I veganized mine and I mentioned this to Kit. I also told her I wonder how really and truly Amish it is after all the morphs it goes through.

One thing is for certain: it's a very forgiving starter and it is DELICIOUS, though I will say this: Everyone LOVES the bread. Not everyone loves to receive the starter because they know this means being in the kitchen. So, bear in mind who you might give this to, if you are ever blessed to receive this starter from one of your friends.

I had a dinner for friends from Chicago visiting Florida. The day of the dinner was also they 10th day of my Amish Bread Process which means that was my baking day.

As I was preparing their dinner, I was also doing the bread thing.

I usually like to give my guests a favor when they come to my house for an occasion. As I was putting the ingredients together, I remembered that I hadn't bought any favors. Suddenly, I had an Ah Hah Moment! I would give them each some Amish Friendship Bread and starter, too. After all, these were childhood and high school friends from years back. What better gift than that? Along with the instructions and the starter, I wrapped several slices of the bread onto a plate and tucked it all into a small shopping bag with tissue paper. Voila! A hostess gift for them all.

You recall my friend, Diana, who does not like to cook? Well, I am giving some of this to our mutual friends who DO like to cook, however, I didn't want Diana to be hurt if I didn't give her any (actually it would have been a favor to her NOT to give her any), so I explained the entire process to her.

Her response, "Oh no, PLEASE don't. Please don't give me any!" I think she was shaking in her boots thinking I might actually give her some which meant she would have had to be in her kitchen. We had a good laugh over this.

Soups

Hot Soup for Cold Days

We've weathered some really cold days in Florida this year. I know no one up north, where it's **really** cold, has any sympathy for us, but gads we were all freezing down here. Our toes and noses were actually numb. Jackets, scarves, turtleneck sweaters, closed in shoes, mind you and even socks we wore.

But, no matter. We took the opportunity to make soups and soups we had. I think I made a different soup nearly every night for weeks.

Invited to a friend's house one afternoon for a meeting, the host asked one of the ladies what she'd have....meaning in the way of a drink. As she rubs her hands together in an effort to keep warm, she said, "Do you have any soup?" Well, she elicited a laugh, but little did any of us know, that's exactly what they had in store. As we took our seats around the room, the hostess passed a tray of cups filled with the creamy Cauliflower and Leek Soup (Page 105). No spoons needed. Just drink from the cup.

I had the girls over for a dinner gathering and in lovely white mugs served the Butternut Squash Soup (Page 108).

Zopa de Tomate (Tomato Soup)

Fresh tomato soup, thick and creamy with NO cream, Ecuador style

Nice, large, red, firm tomatoes, say about 7 or 8, quartered
2 large onions, quartered
1/2 teaspoon garlic powder
A bunch of fresh basil
1 teaspoon Italian seasoning
1 teaspoon Basil
1 teaspoon Oregano
A squirt of Agave nectar
Salt & Pepper

> ***Beautiful soup! Who cares for fish, game, or any other dis h? Who would not give all else for two pennyworth only of beautiful soup?***
> ***—Lewis Carroll***

Sauté tomatoes and onions in a bit of oil or water, for 5 or 10 minutes. Add rest of ingredients and let cook until fairly done. Pour the tomato mixture into a blender. Add a half blender of water and blend well.

Be sure to remove the plastic cap from the cover when blending a hot liquid, and hold a paper towel over the top, just in case.

Pour everything back into the pan and reduce for another 5 or 10 minutes. Garnish with cilantro and serve with bread or croutons of your choice.

Now, here you have a very delicious, nutritious vegan soup. I watched the wonderful Ecuadorians make this special for me at several meals. Muy deliciosa!

Serves 6 - 8

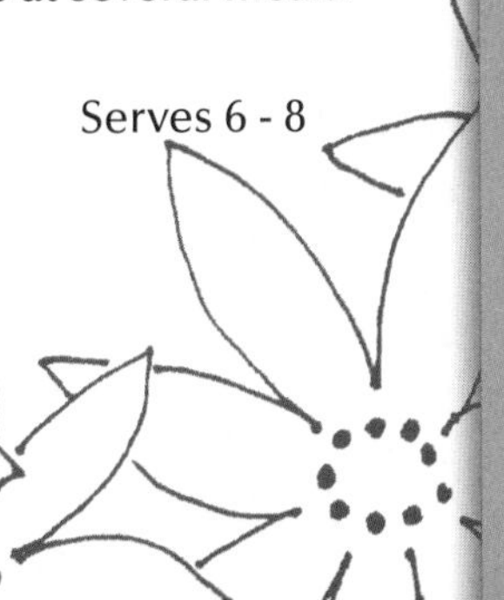

> ***Life expectancy would grow by leaps and bounds if green vegetables smelled as good as bacon.***
>
> ***—Doug Larson***

Thick-and-Creamy-No-Cream-Celery-Soup

1/2 cup water

1 medium onion, chopped

1 medium potato, peeled and chopped

3 - 4 green onions, sliced thin

6 - 7 stalks celery, sliced

3/4 cup dry white wine

4 cups veggie broth

1/2 teaspoon nutmeg

Salt and pepper to taste

Croutons - optional

Sauté onion and potato over medium heat for about 5 minutes.

Add celery and shallots, cook 5 more minutes.

Add wine, boil and cook 3 minutes.

Add broth and water, cover and simmer 20 minutes.

Cool slightly. Puree in blender in batches about a minute a batch.

Return to pot. Bring to boil and turn to simmer immediately. Let reduce for about 5 or 10 minutes. Salt and pepper to taste. Serve with croutons if desired and a nice salad.

Note: Be sure to remove the little plastic top in the cover of the blender before pureeing anything hot. I usually hold a paper towel over the top just for safety sake.

Serves 6 - 8

Many thanks, Susan, for a great soup! Talking about soup on the beach one day, my friend, Susan came to the rescue with this recipe. I veganized it a bit and here it is. Good use of all that celery when you don't know what else to do with it. I love it.

When brainstorming titles for this book, I mentioned the current title to my family.

Kennedy, my nearly 12 year old granddaughter said, "I'm proof of that, Nani. I'm not vegan and I enjoy your recipes." Out of the mouths of babes.

Thank you, dear one.

Cauliflower and Leek Soup

This filled the bill on that uncharacteristically, very cold Florida day. Thank you, JoAnne.

1 bunch cauliflower

2 large leeks

2 garlic cloves, minced

1 (32-ounce) carton vegetable broth

2 cups water

1/2 teaspoon allspice

1/2 teaspoon nutmeg

Sea Salt and Freshly ground pepper

Sauté the cauliflower and leeks in a bit of olive oil in a large pot. Add the vegetable broth and water along with rest of spices and salt and pepper. When cauliflower and leeks are cooked, remove from heat and process in blender until well blended and thick. Return to pot. Bring to boil and simmer another 10 or 15 minutes.

Serves 10 - 12

Thick-and-Creamy-No-Cream-Broccoli-Soup

This soup sort of happened by accident. When I was making the Broccoli Orange Salad one day, I only wanted to use the florets. I cut up all the stems on the fresh broccoli bunch and put them in a baggie in the refrigerator. A few days later, I made the Broccoli Orange Salad again and here I was left with all these stalk pieces. What to do with them? Well, I could cut them up very fine and put them in with the salad, which is exactly what I did with some. The rest I decided to use for Broccoli Soup. Boy! Am I glad I did. This is absolutely delicious! Kennedy and Kerigan even request this. It must be good and not just my thoughts. So, here you go:

Leftover broccoli stalks from the Broccoli Orange Salad or 1 - 2 bunches of fresh broccoli, washed and cut into chunks, stalks and florets.

1 medium onion, coarsely cut

1 (32-ounce) carton of vegetable broth

2 cups water

Sea salt and lots of freshly ground pepper

Put all of the above in a large pan. Bring to a boil then turn down to simmer and let cook until the broccoli is tender. Now, very carefully, ladle all of this into your blender as with the celery and tomato soups. Again, remove the little plastic top in the cover of the blender whenever you are blending anything hot. Blend for about a minute.

Return all liquid to your pot. Bring to boil again and immediately reduce to simmer and let reduce for about 5 or 10 minutes.

Serves 8 - 10

You could also dice the broccoli stalks and sauté in a bit of olive oil with 2 minced garlic cloves. Delicious.

Corn Soup

2 (10-ounce) packages corn

2 cups Almond Milk

1 onion, diced

2 tomatoes, diced

1 small jar pimento strips

2 cups vegetable broth

Salt and Pepper to taste

Blend on high 1 package of corn and the Almond Milk. Set aside. Sauté pimento strips, onion and tomatoes in a bit of water. Add the vegetable broth and finally the blended corn and milk mixture. Heat through and serve with a nice loaf of crusty bread and a salad.

Serves 8 - 10

Avocado Soup, Cold and Refreshing

4 avocados, halved and pitted
3/4 cup frozen sweet peas
1 bunch green onions
Juice of 1 lemon
1/2 bunch cilantro
4 cups vegetable stock
Salt and pepper to taste

> *Worries go down better with soup.*
> *—Jewish Proverb*

Blend all ingredients until smooth. Garnish with sprig of cilantro. Serve cold.

Serves 8 - 10

Sherried-Carrot-Butternut-Squash-Soup

A group of us go to Mt. Dora in the fall every year for a craft show, to browse the wonderful, little-New-England-type-Florida-town with quaint boutiques and antique shops and to just have a fun girls' weekend. A charming tea shop fills to beyond the threshold with people waiting to get in for lunch every day. Their food in general is quite nice, but they have this absolutely-to-die-for carrot soup. Once I became vegan, I stopped eating it because I knew it was made with cream. Well! Here is one I've experimented with that comes every bit as close, if not even better. Von! Take heed.

2 Butternut Squash peeled and cut into chunks

2 large onions, coarsely cut

1 small package of baby carrots or 4 - 5 large carrots cut into 1-inch slices

1 (32-ounce) carton vegetable broth

6 cups water

3/4 cup sherry

1 teaspoon cinnamon

1 teaspoon nutmeg

Sea salt and freshly ground pepper

Sauté butternut squash, onions and carrots in a bit of olive oil in a large pot.

Add vegetable broth, spices and salt and pepper. Simmer until cooked. Remove from heat and process in blender in batches until well blended, about a minute or two. Return to pot. Add sherry and bring to boil then turn down to simmer and cook for another 10 or 15 minutes.

Serve in lovely mugs as an appetizer for your guests.

Serves 12 - 14

Cabbage Soup

1 small head of cabbage, chopped into pieces
1 medium onion, coarsely cut
2 potatoes
1 small bag of baby carrots
1 (28-ounce) can diced tomatoes
1 (32-ounce) carton of vegetable broth
4 cups water
1 package frozen brussel sprouts
1 package frozen corn
1 package frozen peas
Sea salt and freshly ground pepper to taste

Cook all vegetables in the water and vegetable broth until done. Serve with a nice, green salad and a loaf of garlic bread.

Serves 12 - 15

Laden with lots of nutritious vegetables, this is one hearty soup. However, some in my family won't touch it. So what I've done in the past, I've done again and again. Took the lot of it and blended it until thick and creamy. Once it was blended, Kerigan, our little 7 year old had two bowls and loved it, where before she wouldn't touch it. I rather like the presence of vegetables. Gives you something to chew. But for those who do not like the vegetables, blending is a great alternative and they still get their share. Bill would rather have his blended, too.

Desserts

Brownies

These are quite nice, they are!

1 cup oat flour

1 cup whole wheat flour

2 cups sugar

3/4 cups cocoa powder

1 teaspoon baking powder

1 teaspoon salt

1 cup water

1 cup applesauce

1 teaspoon pure vanilla extract

Chopped walnuts

Mix dry ingredients. Add water, oil, vanilla and applesauce. Mix until well blended.

Spread evenly in 9 x 13 inch pan very lightly greased and floured.

Bake 350 ° 25 – 30 minutes or until done.

Serves 12

I will say one thing about the way I've been eating. I don't have the sweet tooth I once had. I can have a taste of cake or a bite of cookie and it satisfies me. Any more than that and it doesn't feel good.

A Valentine Treat Straight From the Heart

My cousin Jeanette lives in Illinois and works as a cook in the kitchen of one of the schools in her area. My Aunt Marge, her mother, emailed and shared the following story with me about a gift Jeanette had planned.

Seems, on one particular day, Jeanette arrived at work at 5:00 a.m., one hour before she was actually scheduled to be there. She gathered all of her baking supplies and equipment and began the process of making Chocolate Chip Cookies for the entire school, 600 in all. Now, this is the fun part. She made them in only 3 batches, one cookie sheet each to go into the 3 large ovens in the school kitchen.

With an ice cream scoop, she plopped the mounds onto the sheets which yielded a good, healthy-sized cookie. A surprise, for sure. The entire school was taken aback, as they had never had such a treat. A Happy Valentine's Day, indeed.

As Jeanette presented her mother, with six cookies solely for her, she related this story and said that the students, teachers, and aides were one bunch of "Happy Campers." Now, that's not only a love for cooking, but also a very determined lady with a heart full of love, not only for what she does but also for those with whom she works.

I must say, I was very impressed. Not only UP at 5 a.m. but IN to work at that hour in the dead of the cold, snow-filled streets of winter, besides. What a great Valentine gift and straight from her heart.

Oatmeal-Raisin-Chewy-Cookies

I love a good, chewy oatmeal cookie and these fill the bill. This is a small recipe, so I usually double it

1/4 cup whole wheat flour
1/4 cup white flour
1/2 teaspoon baking soda
1 cup oats
1/2 cup brown sugar
1/2 cup applesauce
1/4 cup Agave nectar or sugar
1/2 teaspoon cinnamon
1/2 teaspoon salt
2 tablespoons pure vanilla extract
1/2 cup raisins
3/4 cup chopped walnuts

Mix all ingredients together. Drop by spoonful onto cookie sheet. Bake 350° for 12 – 14 minutes.

Doubled makes about 2 dozen

What A Stove!

Speaking of those large, professional restaurant stoves. I had one when we lived at our lake house in Wisconsin. I absolutely LOVED the full-sized cookie sheets that would fit in these ovens. I could get an entire batch of cookies for my family on one or two sheets. It made baking such a breeze.

When we built our home here in Florida, we also incorporated the professional range in our kitchen plans. I had saved my full-sized cookie sheets after all these many years and was so looking forward to the snap of cookie baking again. Well! You can imagine my disappointment when I tried to place the cookie sheets in the oven and they wouldn't fit.

I have a dual range which means the top is gas and the oven is electric for self-cleaning. Seems the added insulation for self-cleaning took up the extra couple of inches needed for those cookie sheets. No one told me that when I ordered it. So, keep that in mind if you buy one of these stoves.

Old Appliances

My Aunt Marge told me the other day that she still has her old, 1947 Westinghouse Refrigerator in her basement. She says it still works and she has never had to replace so much as the rubber door gasket. They just don't make appliances like they used to.

And again, speaking of those large, full-size cake pans. My aunt and uncle used them to dry the parsley and fresh basil which they had grown in their herb garden. "I can still smell the aroma," says Aunt Marge.

She goes on to add, "When we lived on the farm from 1920 to 1937, my Mother cooked on a wood burning stove, which had a large oven and also an area on the side that gave us hot water. She was an excellent cook, and I learned a lot from her.

"I really should have written a book, as my son-in-law suggested." I told her even though she is eighty-five, it's not too late.

Rhubarb-Apple Crisp

If you like tart, you will like this dessert. It's not too tart, just right. Not too sweet, just right.

- 4 cups sliced rhubarb
- 3 cups apples, peeled and sliced
- 1/3 cup Agave nectar
- 1 heaping teaspoon tapioca
- 1 1/4 teaspoons cinnamon
- 1/2 cup whole wheat flour
- 1/2 cup heaping rolled oats
- 5 tablespoons brown sugar
- 1/2 - 3/4 cup chopped pecans or walnuts
- 3 tablespoons pure maple syrup
- Sea salt to taste

Mix rhubarb, apples, Agave nectar, tapioca and cinnamon together. Turn into a 9 x 13 inch pan.

Mix flour, oats, brown sugar, nuts, syrup, and salt until well incorporated. Spread over rhubarb mixture.

Bake 350° 30 to 45 minutes. Serve warm or at room temperature, and top with a scoop of Rice Dream, a non-dairy ice cream.

Serves 10 - 12

A Lovely Warm Fruit Mix to End the Meal

Gather your favorite fruits such as peaches, nectarines, or mangoes and cut into thin slices. Include raspberries, blueberries and blackberries or melons, cantelope, pineapple, any combination, thereof.

Mix your fruits together in an oven proof baking dish. Drizzle Agave Nectar Sweetener over the fruit and place in a 450° oven until fruits are tender, about 20 - 25 minutes or so.

When done, pour a little freshly squeezed orange juice and cinnamon over all and serve warm.

The fruit alone is wonderful or you can serve this over your favorite cake, non-diary ice cream, or the lemon cheesecake (page 116).

Lemon Cheesecake with Graham Cracker Crust

This is lovely and is better made a day ahead. The first time I made this, I served it too soon after baking. Though it was great tasting, it wasn't quite as firm as I would have liked. So, after you have baked it, let it cool and refrigerate overnight. The next day, it cuts and holds its shape beautifully. Serve this with fresh fruit: strawberries, blueberries, blackberries, raspberries or a combination of all four.

Crust

1 1/2 cups organic graham crackers rolled into crumbs

6 Tablespoons vegan butter, melted

1/4 to 1/2 teaspoon cinnamon

1/4 cup Agave sweetener

1/2 to 3/4 cup pecans or walnuts, chopped

Mix all ingredients together until well moistened. Transfer the mixture into a 10-inch pie plate and with the back of a spoon or your fingertips, evenly distribute on the bottom and up the sides of the pan. Bake in a 350° oven until lightly browned, 10 minutes or so. Do not let get too brown as this needs to go into the oven again once it is filled.

While this is baking, prepare the filling.

Filling

4 1/2 teaspoons Ener-G Egg Replacer

6 Tablespoons water

3 (8-ounce) containers non-dairy, non-hydrogenated cream cheese

1 teaspoon vanilla

1/2 to 3/4 cup Agave Sweetener

Zest of two fresh lemons

Juice of two fresh lemons

With a small wire whisk, mix the Egg Replacer with water until smooth. Set aside. In a food processor or mixer, beat the cream cheese until smooth. Add the Egg Replacer and mix again. Finally, add the vanilla, Agave, lemon zest and lemon juice and mix until well incorporated.

Transfer the batter to the cooled graham cracker crust and bake at 350° for 55 to 60 minutes or until done. Let cool for about two hours, then refrigerate overnight. Serve with fresh berries.

Serves 12 - 14 if people request the proverbial sliver.

An Amusing Banana Story

We are on a tram with several others, being transported to the small boat that would carry us to the Panama Canal waters where we would enjoy a one hour tour upfront and close to the monkeys in the rainforest.

We strike up a conversation with Joan and Bob, a couple who are sitting next to us. The first thing I ask is where they are from. Lo and behold, they are from Chicago as we are originally and now Florida, where we also live. Bob and Bill both worked in similar fields and so we have this instant connection. We chit chat all the way to the docking point.

Once there, we all proceed to board the boat. A few minutes into the ride, from two rows back, Bob calls to Bill and hands him two bananas for the "girls," our daughter, Mary Carol, and her former college room-mate, Meg. Meg declines and gives hers to me. What a kind gesture, giving the bananas to us.

Mary Carol and I don't think a thing of it because we are always carrying bananas with us when we are on the road to quell any hunger attacks. In fact, I had brought 6 or 8 organic bananas with me from home all the way to Panama and am now out of them. It is late morning and just the right time for a snack. The bananas are fresh and we proceed to eat them. They do their job and stave the hunger we are experiencing.

When Mary Carol and I turn around to say thank you for the bananas, it hits us—those bananas were to feed the monkeys we were about to visit. Bob and Joan ask, "Don't they feed you girls?" Oh my gosh! I think I feel my face flush. It's red, for sure.

In the end, we all have a good laugh over this.

There are plenty of other bananas on the boat and the monkeys I think are getting their fill.

The boat creeps in close to the shore where tree branches jut out and hang over the water's edge. People throw bananas to the monkeys into the low branches from which they swing. Some of them even hop onto our boat and pluck them from the hands of those who are brave enough to outstretch their arms toward them.

Monkeys in the wild eating bananas from our hands. One exhilarating experience!

Oh! And speaking of bananas, here is a Panamanian dish I hope you will enjoy.

Nutty-Cinnamon-Bananas

A sweet ending to a meal.

2 very ripe bananas

2 tablespoons vegan butter

Drizzle of Agave Sweetener (They used sugar)

1 teaspoon Cinnamon

1/2 cup chopped walnuts

Melt vegan butter in a fry pan. Peel bananas and slice into coins or split in half lengthwise. Fry until golden brown, then add the Agave Sweetener and sprinkle with cinnamon and nuts. Cook over a low heat until they are soft and syrupy.

Rum-Raisin-Bread Pudding, Rich, and Chocolatey

Before I changed my way of eating, I was constantly baking. When my children were little, I used to say that my cookie jar was never empty. My biggest challenge as a vegan was baking without eggs. Seems they are in everything and it was difficult to find a recipe that didn't call for them. I have since discovered they are not really needed with all the wonderful egg replacers that can used instead. I think you'll agree that the dessert recipes within these pages are just as good without them.

2 large loaves of crusty bread, sliced and cut into 1-inch cubes. Set aside in a large bowl.

(I use the crusts and all because I like the chewiness of them.

Some cut the crusts away and only use the inside part of the bread).

5 cups dairy-free milk (Almond, Brown Rice, Oat or Hemp)

1 1/2 cups Agave Sweetener

1 teaspoon salt

1 1/2 teaspoons cinnamon

2 (10-ounce) packages dairy-free, semi-sweet chocolate chips

Egg replacer for 4 eggs

1 cup chopped walnuts

2 tablespoons pure vanilla extract

1/3 cup light or dark rum, your choice

1 cup raisins

Combine the non-dairy milk, Agave, salt and cinnamon in a medium saucepan. Let come to boil and turn down to simmer. Add the chocolate chips and stir until melted. Add egg replacers and finally, add the walnuts, vanilla extract, rum and raisins. Mix well.

Pour this mixture over the bread in the large bowl and again mix well. Let sit for 30 minutes or so until bread is well soaked with chocolate mixture, stirring every so often. Turn it all into a 10 x 15 inch pyrex dish and press down and smooth out the top.

Bake 350° 1 hour or until edges are crispy and a knife or toothpick inserted emerges nearly clean.

Let sit for about 30 minutes before serving.

Serves 16 - 20

My Everything Room

You may be wondering why I would mention an Everything Room when this book is about health and food. You'll see!

Houses in the midwest have basements and the place to which laundry rooms were relegated. It was another place where many large family gatherings were held. It was up and down the steps continually because it was such a huge part of our living. My mother had an entire kitchen in her basement/laundry room for when she entertained large groups.

Instead of basements in Florida, however, many of the homes here house laundry facilities either in their breezeways or garages. A basement is something we sorely miss in Florida. The garages, for us personally at least, take the place of a basement and become storage and laundry rooms.

More recently, builders have begun incorporating laundry rooms in the newer home designs and have begun to give them their own space instead of treating them as an afterthought.

I never could figure out why there wasn't thought given to clothes-folding space. A few allotted feet for the washer and dryer and that was about it. No space planned for the ironing of these clothes either for that matter other than an afterthought of a small fold down board or the hanging of these clothes. I dislike having to grab an armload of laundry from the dryer and transport it to a table or bed to fold it.

The owner and builder of our last house had allowed for an oversized garage. Good planning! When we moved into this house, this space was the width of the two car garage, 26 wonderful feet long and an extra 6 feet in depth. I transformed this space into a very long laundry room and storage room.

I had cabinets installed, planned a hanging area for laundry, counter for folding, and an alcove for the ironing board which never came down. Makes ironing or pressing something a whole lot easier if all I have to do is plug in the iron. There was a place for the refrigerator, and another section for a large trash can. I had plenty of storage and plenty of laundry facility. It was so perfect. I absolutely loved this room. Then, I began using it to store extra food. I like back-ups of everything, so I don't ever run out of particular item when I might need it for a recipe. The refrigerator in the kitchen never seemed to hold enough so I used the second refrigerator for lots of extras too. This room, my office and my kitchen were where I spent the bulk of my day.

Still, it was a make-shift room off the garage. I thought that if we ever built a home, it was going to have a real Everything Room. A place to do craft work, to work on projects, a space for Christmas wrap and everyday wrap, an area to store things, and also the facilities needed to wash and dry clothes. A place for hanging the clothes, for the ironing board to be perpetually set up, a refrigerator, a sink and even a wrapping closet. I mentioned this to a friend one day that if I'd had my druthers, this is what it would be. Her response was, "Carol, that's called a house."

Well, I had my wish. Although we always had very old homes and had done our share of renovating, we had never built one from scratch. And so, the time came when we were blessed with the opportunity to build a house.

The blueprints called my room, Carol's Everything Room. It is large with lots of cabinets and a place for everything. One section houses a cubed bin, for

rolls of wrapping paper, like an architect's box that houses rolled up blueprints. I had a long metal rod installed to hold all the ribbons. When I found that didn't work, I had shelves built on a backward slant for ribbon rolls so they don't come tumbling out. It is a pure luxury for me to be able to open these doors and pluck the appropriate paper and ribbons when I am about to wrap a gift. I'm all about organization and convenience.

This room also has a sink. I can leave my juicer on the counter instead of banishing it to the back of a cupboard. And it is in this room that I make fresh juices. I planned this room and my office to emanate off of my kitchen so that it becomes a triangle and again the three rooms in which I spend the bulk of my day.

My Everything Room does double duty along with the kitchen when entertaining. I store extra food and beverages in the refrigerator. I prepare large salads in here at the last minute instead of in the kitchen where many people like to gather. The sink holds pots, pans or cookie sheets not ready to be washed, just to get the mess out of the kitchen. It is truly an amazing room and I am ever so grateful to have it.

Just for fun, here is a photo of My Everything Room.

My Kitchen

Along the same lines, my kitchen is a jewel, as well, and the mainstay of my day. It's sort of like a large country kitchen. It is comprised of three pantries for an abundance of storage, a wonderful island for lots of food preparation, an expanded table for our immediate family, at least 12, when we are together at the same time for informal gatherings and when we don't quite want to go into the dining room. A large professional range with two full sized ovens bakes and roasts several dishes simultaneously. A full-size, separate refrigerator and yet a full size separate freezer stand next to each other. Meals galore are prepared and eaten in this room, along with lots of family and fun.

I mention all of this because I think anyone who likes to cook and be in the kitchen would appreciate these wonderful rooms. I didn't always have rooms like this and now I do, thank the Good Lord. It's a dream toward which to aspire and sometimes when you least expect it, good things happen and anything is possible.

Here is a photo of my kitchen.

Part Three
One Week of
Sample Menus
Menus

Day 1

Breakfast

Pancakes (p. 90)
with 1/2 cup applesauce

Snack

Fruit

Lunch

Carrot-Butternut Squash Soup (p. 108)

Mixed green salad with tomatoes and freshly squeezed lemon juice

Dinner

Steamed Vegetables:

- Brussel sprouts
- Green beans
- Asparagus

1/2 cup brown rice

Cole Slaw

Day 2

Breakfast

1 cup whole groat oatmeal with
raisins, bananas and chopped pecans,
A drizzle of Agave nectar and a bit of
Almond Milk

Snack

Left over veggies

Lunch

Tabouli salad

Lima beans

Dinner

Chili (p. 68) topped with guacamole, and salsa, served over cooked brown rice with a mixed green salad and tomatoes

Day 3

Breakfast

Muesli (p.90) with sliced bananas and berries

Snack

Fruit Smoothie with several of your favorite fruits and Kale.

Lunch

1 cup Tomato Soup (p. 103)

A Collard Wrap (p. 87)

Snack

1 oz walnuts or raw almonds

Dinner

Avocado Soup (p. 107)

Cabbage Slaw (p. 61)

Brown Rice Medley (p. 99)

Day 4

Breakfast

Chia Seed pudding (p. 92)

Banana

Snack

Kale Chips (p. 49)

Lunch

Cabbage Slaw

Grilled, roasted or steamed asparagus

Dinner

Curried Chickpea Croquettes with
salsa verde (p. 76)

Mixed green salad

Day 5

Breakfast

A Wrap of avocado and tomato slices on Eziekiel,
flourless sprouted grain tortillas

Cooked Kale

Snack

Leftover Chickpea Croquettes with Salsa Verde

Lunch

Beans and Rice (p. 78)

with Homemade Salsa

Dinner

Zucchini Crust Pizza (p. 67)

Mixed green salad

Day 6

Breakfast

Baked Apple with Agave Sweetener, Chopped Walnuts, Raisins and Cinnamon

Lunch

Leftover Zucchini Crust Pizza and a small salad

Snack

Carrot and Celery sticks with hummus

Dinner

Quinoa Paella Without the Meat (p. 72)

Mixed green salad

Day 7

Breakfast

Sometimes I will have a banana, a cup of fresh, unsweetened fruit juice and a glass of lemon water that I sip on throughout the morning. It's plenty filling.

Lunch

Black-eyed Pea Salad (p. 52)

Hummus sandwich on whole grain bread with lettuce, tomatoes, shredded carrots, cucumbers and sunflower sprouts. Or use a collard green for your wrap.

Dinner

Celery Soup (p. 104)

Roasted Potatoes (p. 95)

Mixed green salad

Snack

Fruit

Acknowledgements

My heartfelt thanks goes to:

Marcus Zillman and Jeff Bohr, for their invaluable consulting, computer experience and technological skills which helped us tremendously. Without them and their gifts, I would be lost at the computer.

Stephanie Reed, Stephanie VanArsdall, Angie Jenkins, Nancy Elmore, Carol Walker, Jeff McKee, Melissa McDonald, Kathy Kappel and all those at Pre Media, for their incredible help, guidance, direction, and creativity and the major part they played in getting this book to press.

All my good friends, who encouraged me to write this book (as I had no plan of embarking on such a project, Really!) and to all those who in one way or another cheered me on as I wrote and kept asking how close I was to being finished. It was truly encouraging.

All my good friends with whom I have enjoyed meals, and to all those others who contributed recipes which added to the entirety of this book: Charlotte Athy, Barbara Desano, Barbara Goduti, Barbara Lindner, Frances Moore, Maria Saez, April Scarlott, and Susan Shuster (I hope I haven't left anyone out. Please forgive me if I did).

Kerigan, Will and Marley, our younger set and even though they're too young to realize it, for their constant source of inspiration.

Kennedy, our twelve year old granddaughter, for her help filming my videos to be used in conjunction with the book and the website, for her constant interest, suggestions, direction and valid, valued, and worthwhile opinions, which seem to be never-ending and amaze us all.

Sabrina, our beautiful daughter-in-law, for her support, her interest in good health, and for her always forward-looking optimism.

My wonderful sons, Patrick, Daniel and William for all their support, encouragement and pats on the back. It's truly heartwarming.

My beautiful daughters, Keri and Mary Carol, for their amazing photography skills, for all the uploading of photographs when we needed them, for their willing offers to help and for their talents, their creative design and critical eye. They see things I do not see. I am so proud of them and whether they know it or not, I learn from them, as I do from my sons and even my grandchildren.

My husband, Bill, who is a continual and perpetual encourager, for his never-ending compliments, gentleness, generosity, understanding, and kindness and who couldn't be more proud of all of our accomplishments. A true cheerleader!

My devoted and generous Mother, a great cook in her own right, who made it all seem so effortless, who would give the food off of her plate, for her enduring love and who instilled in me my desire for cooking and that the kitchen is the true heart of the home. She is 95, with severe dementia, and I am sad she doesn't have the full realization or can really enjoy this book. I know she would if she could. I salute her.

It's been a labor of love and without you, major pieces would have been missing.

Thank you ALL from the bottom of my heart!

Most of all, I give thanks to my God, the Good Lord, for the gifts and blessings he has given me, who is in my heart, with me always and my constant source of peace, renewal and inspiration.

Resources

Books

I would highly recommend any of these books if you are on a quest. Even if you aren't, they are rife with fabulous, well documented information that you just don't hear about in mainstream circles.

Brain Trust, Colm A. Kelleher - (The book that started this whole thing for me. I turned the last page and cover on this book and that was the beginning of the end of my eating beef and pork).

Raising Vegan Children in a Non-Vegan World, Erin Pavlina

The China Study, T. Colin Campbell and Thomas M. Campbell, ("One of the largest and most comprehensive studies ever undertaken of the relationship between diet and the risk of developing disease." New York Times; "A monumental survey of diet and death rates from cancer in more than 2400 Chinese counties," Frank Rhodes, PhD, President Emeritus, Cornell University). T. Colin Campbell is one of the gargantuan leaders in the field.

The Rave Diet, Mike Anderson

Dr. John McDougall - Newsletters for which you can sign up free on his website. He has a wealth of information in his Hot Topics area.

Other books by Dr. John McDougall:

Digestive Tune-up

The McDougall Program

The Mcdougall Plan

Diet for A New America, John Robbins, (The Robbins of Baskin-Robbins who gave up his entire ice cream fortune for a better way of life and became a vegan).

The Food Revolution, John Robbins

Seeds of Deception, Jeffrey M. Smith

Mad Cowboy, Howard Lyman, (who grew up on a dairy farm and became a cattle rancher, who later turned vegan, for the health benefits. He is also the one who was sued with Oprah Winfrey by the Texas Cattle Ranchers. They won!).

The Mad Cowboy Newsletter, Howard Lyman

No More Bull, Howard Lyman

Death by Diet, Robert R. Barefoot

Healing Inflammatory Bowel Disease, Paul Nison

Mucusless Diet Healing System, Arnold Ehret

Dr. Neal Barnard's Program for Reversing Diabetes, Dr. Neal D. Barnard

The Complete Encyclopedia of Natural Healing, Gary Null, Ph. D.

Healing the Gerson Way: Defeating Cancer and Other Chronic Diseases, Charlotte Gerson with Beata Bishop

Milk A - Z, Robert Cohen

Natural Cures "They" Don't Want You To Know About, Kevin Trudeau

The Better Brain Book, David Perlmutter, M. D. and Carol Colman

Quantum Wellness, Kathy Freston

Disease-Proof Your Child, Joel Fuhrman, M. D.

Juice Fasting and Detoxification, Steve Meyerowitz

Websites:

http://www.dorway.com/badnews.html

http://www.dorway.com/thetoxins.html

http://www.dorway.com/bressler.txt

Dr. Russell Blaylock, Natural Strategies for Cancer Patients
Blaylock Wellness Report

blaylockreport.com, Russell blaylock, Oncologist, brain surgeon, and neuroscientist

www.garynull.com.

www.madcowboy.com

www.responsibletechnology.org, Jeffrey M. Smith, Executive Director of the Institute for Responsible Technology and the leading spokesperson on the health dangers of GMOs. Author of *Seeds of Deception* which is the world's bestselling book on the subject. Also Author of *Genetic Roulette: The Documented health Risks of Genetically Engineered Foods*. This book identifies 65 risks of GMOs and demonstrates how superficial government approvals are not competent to find most of them.

DVDs

Wake Up and Get Healthy, A Gary Null Production

Overcoming Cardiovascular Disease Naturally, A Gary Null Production

Gary Null's Seven Steps to Total Health, A Gary Null Production

Age is Only A Number, A Gary Null Production
Gary Null, Ph.D., scientist, lecturer, and author of more than 70 books.

Healing Cancer from the Inside Out, Mike Anderson

Dr. McDougall's Common Sense Nutrition

McDougall Made Easy

McDougall Made Irresistible

McDougall's Medicine

Dr. McDougall's Total Health Solution for the 21st Century

Dr. McDougall Disputes Major Medical Treatments

The Future of Food, Documentary

The GMO Trilogy, Documentary

The Beautiful Truth, Documentary

Mad Cowboy, The Documentary

Creative Low-Fat Vegan Cuisine, Jill Nussinow, R. D.

The Gerson Miracle, Kroschel Films

The Gerson Therapy: Healing "Incurable" Illness, Volume I

The Gerson Therapy: Healing "Incurable" Illness, Volume II

Sweet Misery: A Poisoned World, Documentary

Endnotes

1. Joel Fuhrman, M.D., *Disease-Proof Your Child:Feeding Kids Right,* (New York: St. Martin's Press, 2005), p. 13.
2. Ibid. p. 13.
3. T. Colin Campbell, *The China Study,* (Dallas: BenBella Books, 2004), p. 233.
4. Ibid, p. 234.
5. Neal D. Barnard, M.D., *Dr. Neal Barnard's Program for Reversing Diabetes,* (New York: Rodale, 2007), p. 66.
6. Ibid, p. 31.

7. http://www.vrg.org/nutrition/protein.htm#table1
8. Frances Moore Lappe, *Diet for a Small Planet,* (New York: Ballantine Books, 1991).
9. Dr. David Perlmutter, *The Better Brain Book,* (New York: Riverhead books, 2004), p. 147.
10. http://www.sfgate.com/cgi-bin/article.cgi?f=/c/a/2002/11/05/MN93684.DTL
11. http://www.journeytoforever.org/farm_library/bobsmith.html and John Robbins, Diet for a New America, (Maine: Conari Press, 2001), p. 371.
12. T. Colin Campbell, PhD, The China Study, *(Dallas:BenBella Books, 2004), p. 138.*
13. Ibid, p. 136.
14. Gary Null, Ph.D., *The Complete Encyclopedia of Natural Healing,* (New York: Kensington Books, 1998, 2005), p. 409.
15. Neal Barnard, M.D., *Dr. Neal Barnard's Program for Reversing Diabetes,* (New York: Rodale, 2007), p. 127
16. Gary Null, Ph.D., *The Complete Encyclopedia of Natural Healing,* (New York: Kensington Books, 1998, 2005), p. 324.
17. http://www.dorway.com/jcohen.html
18. Dr. Russell Blaylock, in the film *Sweet Misery: A Poisoned World.*
19. http://www.dorway.com/bmartini.html
20. Neal Barnard, M.D., Dr. *Neal Barnard's Program for Reversing Diabetes,* (New York: Rodale, 2007), p. 52.
21. www.Greenandsave.com
22. Neal Barnard, M.D., Dr. *Neal Barnard's Program for Reversing Diabetes,* (New York: Rodale, 2007) p. 14-15.
23. Life Extension Foundation, *Disease Prevention and Treatment,* (Hollywood:Life Extension Media, 1997-2003), p. 718.
24. http://www.shapefit.com/sources-carbohydrates.html
25. *Robert Cohen, Milk A - Z,* (New Jersey:Argus Publishing, 2001), p. 32.
26. *Science*, 1986, p. 233.
27. Neal Barnard, M.D., Dr. *Neal Barnard's Program for Reversing Diabetes,* (New York: Rodale, 2007), p.135.
28. Dr. John McDougall, *McDougall Newsletter,* Vol. 6, No. 11, November, 2007.
29. Ibid.
30. Very edited from the statistic-packed essay at: http://www.alternet.org/water/134650/ the_startling_effects_of _going_vegetarian_for_just_one_day/ 4/02/09.
31. http://www.sunnylandmills.com/little_known_facts_bulgur.html
32. Ibid.

Index

A

Adobo Goya seasoning
Beans and Rice *78*

Agave
A Colorful Pepper-Corn-and-Bean-Dip *45*
Agave Nectar *25*
A-Hearty-No-Meat-Chock-Full-of-Vegetables-Good-For-You-Chili *68*
A Lovely Warm Fruit Mix to End the Meal *115*
Baked Artichoke Hearts with Tomatoes & Onions *97*
Cabbage Slaw *61*
Chia Seed Pudding *92*
Crunch-Salad with-Black-Eyed Peas *52*
Italian Pasta Sauce *82*
Lemon Cheesecake with Graham Cracker Crust *116*
Mango Slaw *62*
Nutty-Cinnamon-Bananas *118*
Oatmeal-Raisin-Chewy-Cookies *112*
Orange-Broccoli-Carrot-and-Raisin-Salad *51*
Peas, Shoe Peg Corn and Green Bean Salad *53*
Ramen Noodle Slaw Mix *63*
Rhubarb-Apple Crisp *114*
Rum-Raisin-Bread Pudding, Rich, and Chocolatey *119*
Slightly-Nutty-Non-Dairy-No-Egg-Pancakes *90*
Thai Noodles, Creamy and Peanutty *74*

Allspice
Cauliflower and Leek Soup *105*
Pasta with Mushrooms and Tomato Sauce *70*
Spinach with Tomatoes and Potatoes *86*

Almond milk
Almond Milk *25*
Chia Seed Pudding *92*
Corn Soup *106*
Slightly-Nutty-Non-Dairy-No-Egg-Pancakes *90*

Almonds
almonds *40*
Artichoke Spread *44*
Ramen Noodle Slaw Mix *63*

American Academy of Environmental Medicine *35*

American Dietetic Association *21*

Amish Friendship Bread *101*

An Amusing Banana Story *117*

Animal foods *13, 37*

Animal protein *20, 33*

Appetizers
A Colorful Pepper-Corn-and-Bean-Dip *45*
Artichokes Italian-Style a la Connie *44*
Artichoke Spread *44*
Eggplant and Zucchini Bruschetta *47*
Guacamole *43*
Kale Chips *49*
Marinated Green Olive Nibbles *49*
Marvelous Marinated Mushrooms *46*
Pine Nut Pesto *45*
Red Bell Pepper Spread *46*
Traditional Tomato Bruschetta *48*

Apples
Apples *25*
Cabbage Slaw *61*
Rhubarb-Apple Crisp *114*

Applesauce
Brownies *111*
Oatmeal-Raisin-Chewy-Cookies *112*
Slightly-Nutty-Non-Dairy-No-Egg-Pancakes *90*

Artichoke hearts
artichoke hearts *26*
Artichoke Spread *44*
Baked Artichoke Hearts with Tomatoes & Onions *97*
Everything-But-the-Kitchen-Sink-Salad *60*
Quinoa Paella without the Meat *72*

Artichokes
Artichokes Italian-Style a la Connie *44*

Asparagus
Cold, Refreshing Asparagus Salad *59*

Aspartame *27–29*

Associative Culture *22*

Avocado
Avocado *22*
Avocado Soup, Cold and Refreshing *107*
Collard Wraps *87*
Corn and Avocado Salad *58*
Crunch-Salad with-Black-Eyed Peas *52*
Guacamole *43*

B

B12 *34, 37*

Baby carrots
Cabbage Soup *109*
Sherried-Carrot-Butternut-Squash-Soup *108*

Baby peas
Tomatoes Filled with Minted Peas *98*

Baking powder
Brownies *111*
Pakoras *75*
Slightly-Nutty-Non-Dairy-No-Egg-Pancakes *90*
Various Egg Replacers *93*

Baking soda
Oatmeal-Raisin-Chewy-Cookies *112*
Various Egg Replacers *93*

Balsamic vinegar
Red Bell Pepper Spread *46*

Banana
An Amusing Banana Story *117*
Fruit Smoothie, Delicious and Healthy *91*
Nutty-Cinnamon-Bananas *118*
Various Egg Replacers *93*

Barley
barley *32*
Barley-Corn-and-Kidney-Bean-Salad *55*

Basil
A-Hearty-No-Meat-Chock-Full-of-Vegetables-Good-For-You-Chili *68*
Baked Artichoke Hearts with Tomatoes & Onions *97*
Cold, Refreshing Asparagus Salad *59*
Eggplant and Zucchini Bruschetta *47*
Green-Beans-Tomatoes-and-Lots-of-Wonderful-Basil-Salad *51*
Italian Pasta Sauce *82*
Pasta with Mushrooms and Tomato Sauce *70*
Pine Nut Pesto *45*
Red Bell Pepper Spread *46*
Roasted Potatoes *95*
Salsa Verde *77*
Traditional Tomato Bruschetta *48*
Zopa de Tomate (Tomato Soup) *103*

Bay leaves
Beans and Rice *78*
Italian Pasta Sauce *82*
Pasta with Mushrooms and Tomato Sauce *70*

Bean burrito *26*

Beans
A Colorful Pepper-Corn-and-Bean-Dip *45*
A-Hearty-No-Meat-Chock-Full-of-Vegetables-Good-For-You-Chili *68*
Barley-Corn-and-Kidney-Bean-Salad *55*
Bean and Corn Casserole *81*
Beans and Rice *78*
Bulgur Wheat-Mint-Parsley-and-Cilantro-Salad (AKA Tabouli) *56*
Green-Beans-Tomatoes-and-Lots-of-Wonderful-Basil-Salad *51*
Mung Bean Salad *54*
Peas, Shoe Peg Corn and Green Bean Salad *53*
Quinoa Paella without the Meat *72*
Southwestern Corn Salad *58*

Besin flour
Pakoras *75*

Black beans
A Colorful Pepper-Corn-and-Bean-Dip *45*
Bean and Corn Casserole *81*
Corn and Avocado Salad *58*
Southwestern Corn Salad *58*

Blackberries
Fruit Smoothie, Delicious and Healthy *91*
Lemon Cheesecake with Graham Cracker Crust *116*

Black-eyed peas
Crunch-Salad with-Black-Eyed Peas *52*

Bone loss *32*

Brain tumors *28*

Bread
Eggplant and Zucchini Bruschetta *47*
Red Bell Pepper Spread *46*

Bread crumbs
Artichokes Italian-Style a la Connie *44*

Breakfast Foods
Chia Seed Pudding *92*
Fruit Smoothie, Delicious and Healthy *91*
Lemon Water *93*
Muesli *90*
Slightly-Nutty-Non-Dairy-No-Egg-Pancakes *90*
Various Egg Replacers *93*
Whole Oat Groat Oatmeal *92*

Broccoli
Broccoli Ala Orange *95*
Orange-Broccoli-Carrot-and-Raisin-Salad *51*
Thick-and-Creamy-No-Cream-Broccoli-Soup *106*
Zucchini Crust Pizza With Lots of Wonderful Toppings *67*

Brown rice
A-Hearty-No-Meat-Chock-Full-of-Vegetables-Good-For-You-Chili *68*
Bean and Corn Casserole *81*
Beans and Rice *78*
brown rice *20, 31*
Brown Rice Medley *99*
Brown Rice with Corn and Peas *84*
Brown Rice with Dill and Tomatoes *85*
Rum-Raisin-Bread Pudding, Rich, and Chocolatey *119*
Split Peas and Pasta *71*
Tabouli Tabbouleh Taboli Tabouleh Taboule *56*
Thai Noodles, Creamy and Peanutty *74*
Wild Rice Pilaf *53*

Brown rice milk *33*

Brown rice pasta
brown rice pasta *31*
Pasta with Mushrooms and Tomato Sauce *70*

Brown rice spaghetti
Thai Noodles, Creamy and Peanutty *74*

Brussel sprouts
Bulgur Wheat-Mint-Parsley-and-Cilantro-Salad *56*
Cabbage Soup *109*

Bulgur
bulgur *31*
Bulgur Wheat-Mint-Parsley-and-Cilantro-Salad (AKA Tabouli) *56*
Tabouli Tabbouleh Taboli Tabouleh Taboule *56*

Butternut squash
Hot Soup for Cold Days *103*
Sherried-Carrot-Butternut-Squash-Soup *108*

B vitamins
B vitamins *27*
Chia Seed Pudding *92*
Tabouli Tabbouleh Taboli Tabouleh Taboule *56*

C

Calcium
calcium *20, 32, 40, 91*
Chia Seed Pudding *92*

Cancer *15, 28, 32*

Capers
Salsa Verde *77*

Carrots
Brown Rice Medley *99*
Brown Rice with Corn and Peas *84*
Cabbage Soup *109*
Collard Wraps *87*
Orange-Broccoli-Carrot-and-Raisin-Salad *51*
Sherried-Carrot-Butternut-Squash-Soup *108*
Thai Noodles, Creamy and Peanutty *74*
Wheatberry Salad *57*
Wild Rice Pilaf *53*

Cauliflower
Cauliflower and Leek Soup *105*
Hot Soup for Cold Days *103*
Pakoras *75*

Cayenne
Cabbage Slaw *61*
Split Peas and Pasta *71*

Cayenne powder
Mung Bean Salad *54*

CDC *28*

Celery
A-Hearty-No-Meat-Chock-Full-of-Vegetables-Good-For-You-Chili *68*
Barley-Corn-and-Kidney-Bean-Salad *55*
Brown Rice Medley *99*
Collard Wraps *87*
Gazpacho *64*
Marinated Green Olive Nibbles *49*
Mung Bean Salad *54*
Peas, Shoe Peg Corn and Green Bean Salad *53*
Thick-and-Creamy-No-Cream-Celery-Soup *104*
Wild Rice Pilaf *53*

Chard
chard *34*
Split Peas and Pasta *71*

Chia seeds
Chia Seed Pudding *92*
chia seeds *31, 34*

Chicken *13, 14, 19, 30, 38*

Chickpea flour
Pakoras *75*

Chick peas
chick peas *20*
Curried Chickpea Croquettes with Salsa Verde *76*

Chili powder
A-Hearty-No-Meat-Chock-Full-of-Vegetables-Good-For-You-Chili *68*
Spinach with Tomatoes and Potatoes *86*

Chili sauce
Thai Noodles, Creamy and Peanutty *74*

Chocolate chips
Rum-Raisin-Bread Pudding, Rich, and Chocolatey *119*

Cholesterol *30, 31, 32, 40, 56*

Chunky tomato sauce
Bean and Corn Casserole *81*

Cilantro
Avocado Soup, Cold and Refreshing *107*
Barley-Corn-and-Kidney-Bean-Salad *55*
Beans and Rice *78*
Bulgur Wheat-Mint-Parsley-and-Cilantro-Salad (AKA Tabouli) *56*
Cold, Refreshing Asparagus Salad *59*
Gazpacho *64*
Guacamole *43*
Mango Slaw *62*
Southwestern Corn Salad *58*
Split Peas and Pasta *71*
Tomato Salsa *78*

Cinnamon
A-Hearty-No-Meat-Chock-Full-of-Vegetables-Good-For-You-Chili *68*
A Lovely Warm Fruit Mix to End the Meal *115*
Chia Seed Pudding *92*
Lemon Cheesecake with Graham Cracker Crust *116*
Muesli *90*
Nutty-Cinnamon-Bananas *118*
Oatmeal-Raisin-Chewy-Cookies *112*
Rhubarb-Apple Crisp *114*
Rum-Raisin-Bread Pudding, Rich, and Chocolatey *119*
Sherried-Carrot-Butternut-Squash-Soup *108*
Whole Oat Groat Oatmeal *92*

Cocoa powder
A-Hearty-No-Meat-Chock-Full-of-Vegetables-Good-For-You-Chili *68*
Brownies *111*

Collard greens
Collard Wraps *87*
Split Peas and Pasta *71*

Collard Wraps *87*

Complex carbohydrates *27, 31, 32*

Constipation *31, 33*

Conventional food *23*

Corn
A Colorful Pepper-Corn-and-Bean-Dip *45*
A-Hearty-No-Meat-Chock-Full-of-Vegetables-Good-For-You-Chili *68*
Barley-Corn-and-Kidney-Bean-Salad *55*
Bean and Corn Casserole *81*
Brown Rice Medley *99*
Brown Rice with Corn and Peas *84*
Brown Rice with Dill and Tomatoes *85*
Cabbage Soup *109*
corn *22, 35*
Corn and Avocado Salad *58*
Corn Soup *106*
Peas, Shoe Peg Corn and Green Bean Salad *53*
Quinoa Paella without the Meat *72*
Southwestern Corn Salad *58*

Corn chips
Bean and Corn Casserole *81*

Couscous
Nutty-Couscous-with-Mint-and-Tomatoes *83*

Crackers
A Colorful Pepper-Corn-and-Bean-Dip *45*
Artichoke Spread *44*
crackers *24*
Pine Nut Pesto *45*
Red Bell Pepper Spread *46*

Craisins
Everything-But-the-Kitchen-Sink-Salad *60*

Cranberries
Bulgur Wheat-Mint-Parsley-and-Cilantro-Salad (AKA Tabouli) *56*
Cabbage Slaw *61*
Collard Wraps *87*
cranberries *25*
Muesli *90*
Ramen Noodle Slaw Mix *63*
Wild Rice Pilaf *53*

Croutons
Thick-and-Creamy-No-Cream-Celery-Soup *104*
Zopa de Tomate (Tomato Soup) *103*

Crusty bread
Corn Soup *106*
Rum-Raisin-Bread Pudding, Rich, and Chocolatey *119*

Cucumber
cucumber *51*
Bulgur Wheat-Mint-Parsley-and-Cilantro-Salad (AKA Tabouli) *56*
Gazpacho *64*

Cumin
A-Hearty-No-Meat-Chock-Full-of-Vegetables-Good-For-You-Chili *68*
Barley-Corn-and-Kidney-Bean-Salad *55*
Bean and Corn Casserole *81*
Brown Rice with Corn and Peas *84*
Curried Chickpea Croquettes with Salsa Verde *76*
Pakoras *75*
Spinach with Tomatoes and Potatoes *86*
Split Peas and Pasta *71*

Currants
Bulgur Wheat-Mint-Parsley-and-Cilantro-Salad (AKA Tabouli) *56*
Nutty-Couscous-with-Mint-and-Tomatoes *83*
Wheatberry Salad *57*

Curry powder
Curried Chickpea Croquettes with Salsa Verde *76*

D

Dairy *14, 18, 19, 32, 34*

Dark green leafy vegetables *22, 31*

Dark rum
Rum-Raisin-Bread Pudding, Rich, and Chocolatey *119*

Delaney Act *28*

Desserts
A Lovely Warm Fruit Mix to End the Meal *115*
Brownies *111*
Lemon Cheesecake with Graham Cracker Crust *116*
Nutty-Cinnamon-Bananas *118*
Oatmeal-Raisin-Chewy-Cookies *112*
Rhubarb-Apple Crisp *114*
Rum-Raisin-Bread Pudding, Rich, and Chocolatey *119*

Diabetes *14, 16, 18, 31, 32, 39*

Diarrhea *33*

Diet soda *27*

Digestive Issues *32*

Digestive symptoms *33*

Dijon mustard
Brown Rice with Dill and Tomatoes *85*
Cabbage Slaw *61*
Cold, Refreshing Asparagus Salad *59*
Mango Slaw *62*
Salsa Verde *77*

Dill
Artichoke Spread *44*
Brown Rice with Dill and Tomatoes *85*

Diverticulosis *32*

Dressings
A Colorful Pepper-Corn-and-Bean-Dip *45*
Barley-Corn-and-Kidney-Bean-Salad *55*
Cold, Refreshing Asparagus Salad *59*
Mango Slaw *62*

Dried apricots *34*

Dried fruit
Everything-But-the-Kitchen-Sink-Salad *60*

E

Eggplant
Eggplant and Zucchini Bruschetta *47*
Traditional Tomato Bruschetta *48*

Egg replacer
Lemon Cheesecake with Graham Cracker Crust *116*
Rum-Raisin-Bread Pudding, Rich, and Chocolatey *119*
Slightly-Nutty-Non-Dairy-No-Egg-Pancakes *90*
Various Egg Replacers *93*
Zucchini Crust Pizza With Lots of Wonderful Toppings *67*

Elbow macaroni
Peas and Macaroni *80*

Ener G Egg Replacer
Various Egg Replacers *93*

Entrees
A-Hearty-No-Meat-Chock-Full-of-Vegetables-Good-For-You-Chili *68*
Bean and Corn Casserole *81*
Beans and Rice *78*
Brown Rice with Corn and Peas *84*
Brown Rice with Dill and Tomatoes *85*
Collard Wraps *87*
Curried Chickpea Croquettes with Salsa Verde *76*
Italian Pasta Sauce *82*
Nutty-Couscous-with-Mint-and-Tomatoes *83*
Pakoras *75*
Pasta with Mushrooms and Tomato Sauce *70*
Peas and Macaroni *80*
Quinoa Paella without the Meat *72*
Salsa Verde *77*
Spinach with Tomatoes and Potatoes *86*
Split Peas and Pasta *71*
Thai Noodles, Creamy and Peanutty *74*
Tomato Salsa *78*
Zucchini Crust Pizza With Lots of Wonderful Toppings *67*

Equal *27*

Essential fatty acids *22, 31*

Essential nutrients *27*

Evaporated Sugar Cane Juice *29*

Eye Opening Statistics *38*

F

Fat *15, 16, 18, 22, 24, 30, 31, 33, 40*

Fatigue *33*

FDA Report *28*

Figs *34*

Finding the Time, then Making It *73*

Fish *13, 14, 19, 21, 24, 30, 31*

Flat Italian green beans
Flat Italian Green Beans and Tomatoes with Greek Seasoning *96*

Flax meal
Fruit Smoothie, Delicious and Healthy *91*

Flax seeds
flax seeds *31*
Fruit Smoothie, Delicious and Healthy *91*
Various Egg Replacers *93*

Flour
Broccoli Ala Orange *95*
flour *27, 31, 32, 37, 40*
Oatmeal-Raisin-Chewy-Cookies *112*
Various Egg Replacers *93*

Formaldehyde *27, 28*

Freedom of Information Act *28*

Fresh basil
- A-Hearty-No-Meat-Chock-Full-of-Vegetables-Good-For-You-Chili *68*
- Baked Artichoke Hearts with Tomatoes & Onions *97*
- Chilled Asparagus Salad *63*
- Cold, Refreshing Asparagus Salad *59*
- Eggplant and Zucchini Bruschetta *47*
- Green-Beans-Tomatoes-and-Lots-of-Wonderful-Basil-Salad *51*
- Italian Pasta Sauce *82*
- Pasta with Mushrooms and Tomato Sauce *70*
- Pine Nut Pesto *45*
- Salsa Verde *77*
- Traditional Tomato Bruschetta *48*
- Zopa de Tomate (Tomato Soup) *103*

G

Garbanzo beans
- A-Hearty-No-Meat-Chock-Full-of-Vegetables-Good-For-You-Chili *68*

Garlic
- Artichoke Spread *44*
- Barley-Corn-and-Kidney-Bean-Salad *55*
- Brown Rice Medley *99*
- Brown Rice with Corn and Peas *84*
- Cauliflower and Leek Soup *105*
- Crunch-Salad with-Black-Eyed Peas *52*
- Curried Chickpea Croquettes with Salsa Verde *76*
- Eggplant and Zucchini Bruschetta *47*
- garlic *25*
- Gazpacho *64*
- Marinated Green Olive Nibbles *49*
- Pasta with Mushrooms and Tomato Sauce *70*
- Pine Nut Pesto *45*
- Quinoa Paella without the Meat *72*
- Salsa Verde *77*
- Spinach with Tomatoes and Potatoes *86*
- Split Peas and Pasta *71*
- Thai Noodles, Creamy and Peanutty *74*
- Traditional Tomato Bruschetta *48*

Garlic powder
- A-Hearty-No-Meat-Chock-Full-of-Vegetables-Good-For-You-Chili *68*
- Artichokes Italian-Style a la Connie *44*
- Beans and Rice *78*
- garlic powder *25*
- Roasted Potatoes *95*
- Spinach with Tomatoes and Potatoes *86*
- Zopa de Tomate (Tomato Soup) *103*

Genes
- genes *16, 34*
- Letter to My Children *39*

Genetically Modified Foods *34*

Ginger
- Spinach with Tomatoes and Potatoes *86*
- Thai Noodles, Creamy and Peanutty *74*

Glycemic index *29, 30, 82*

GM foods *34, 35, 36*

Graham crackers
- Lemon Cheesecake with Graham Cracker Crust *116*

Grains *20, 23, 31, 32, 37*

Green beans
- Bulgur Wheat-Mint-Parsley-and-Cilantro-Salad (AKA Tabouli) *56*
- Flat Italian Green Beans and Tomatoes with Greek Seasoning *96*
- Green-Beans-Tomatoes-and-Lots-of-Wonderful-Basil-Salad *51*
- Peas, Shoe Peg Corn and Green Bean Salad *53*

Green chilies
- A-Hearty-No-Meat-Chock-Full-of-Vegetables-Good-For-You-Chili *68*

Green olives
- Marinated Green Olive Nibbles *49*
- Zucchini Crust Pizza With Lots of Wonderful Toppings *67*

Green onions
- Avocado Soup, Cold and Refreshing *107*
- Baked Artichoke Hearts with Tomatoes & Onions *97*
- Barley-Corn-and-Kidney-Bean-Salad *55*
- Bean and Corn Casserole *81*
- Brown Rice with Corn and Peas *84*
- Brown Rice with Dill and Tomatoes *85*
- Bulgur Wheat-Mint-Parsley-and-Cilantro-Salad (AKA Tabouli) *56*
- Cold, Refreshing Asparagus Salad *59*
- Collard Wraps *87*
- Crunch-Salad with-Black-Eyed Peas *52*
- Gazpacho *64*
- Guacamole *43*
- Nutty-Couscous-with-Mint-and-Tomatoes *83*
- Peas, Shoe Peg Corn and Green Bean Salad *53*
- Ramen Noodle Slaw Mix *63*
- Thai Noodles, Creamy and Peanutty *74*
- Thick-and-Creamy-No-Cream-Celery-Soup *104*
- Tomato Salsa *78*
- Wheatberry Salad *57*
- Wild Rice Pilaf *53*

Green peppers
A-Hearty-No-Meat-Chock-Full-of-Vegetables-Good-For-You-Chili *68*
Everything-But-the-Kitchen-Sink-Salad *60*
Zucchini Crust Pizza With Lots of Wonderful Toppings *67*

H

Heart disease *14, 15, 16, 31, 32, 39*

Hearts of palm
Everything-But-the-Kitchen-Sink-Salad *60*

Hemp milk *33*

Homemade salsa
Bean and Corn Casserole *81*
Beans and Rice *78*

How Hogs Were Raised and Cured *100*

How to Cook for Non-Vegan Friends and Family *79*

I

Idaho potato
Roasted Potatoes *95*

Immune system *27, 34*

Intestinal problems *32*

Italian seasoning
Eggplant and Zucchini Bruschetta *47*
Italian Pasta Sauce *82*
Roasted Potatoes *95*
Zopa de Tomate (Tomato Soup) *103*

I've Come A Long Way *65*

J

Jalapeno pepper
Southwestern Corn Salad *58*

Jicama *25*

K

Kalamata olives
Red Bell Pepper Spread *46*

Kale
Fruit Smoothie, Delicious and Healthy *91*
kale *34*
Kale Chips *49*
Marinated Green Olive Nibbles *49*
Split Peas and Pasta *71*

Kamut *31*

Kelp
Corn and Avocado Salad *58*

Kidney beans
A-Hearty-No-Meat-Chock-Full-of-Vegetables-Good-For-You-Chili *68*
Barley-Corn-and-Kidney-Bean-Salad *55*
Quinoa Paella without the Meat *72*

L

Lactose *33*

Lactose intolerance *33*

Leeks
Cauliflower and Leek Soup *105*

Lemon
Artichokes Italian-Style a la Connie *44*
Artichoke Spread *44*
Avocado Soup, Cold and Refreshing *107*
Bulgur Wheat-Mint-Parsley-and-Cilantro-Salad (AKA Tabouli) *56*
Cabbage Slaw *61*
Cold, Refreshing Asparagus Salad *59*
Crunch-Salad with-Black-Eyed Peas *52*
Gazpacho *64*
Guacamole *43*
Lemon Cheesecake with Graham Cracker Crust *116*
Lemon Water *93*
Mung Bean Salad *54*
Tomatoes Filled with Minted Peas *98*

Lentils *20, 32, 56*

Letter to My Children *39*

Lime
Barley-Corn-and-Kidney-Bean-Salad *55*
Southwestern Corn Salad *58*
Strawberry-Mango Salad *62*
Tomato Salsa *78*

M

Mandarin oranges
Everything-But-the-Kitchen-Sink-Salad *60*

Mango
A Lovely Warm Fruit Mix to End the Meal *115*
Mango Slaw *62*
Strawberry-Mango Salad *62*

Milk *25, 33, 34*

Milk substitutes *33*

Minerals in organic food *23*

Mint
- Artichokes Italian-Style a la Connie *44*
- Bulgur Wheat-Mint-Parsley-and-Cilantro-Salad (AKA Tabouli) *56*
- Curried Chickpea Croquettes with Salsa Verde *76*
- Nutty-Couscous-with-Mint-and-Tomatoes *83*
- Pakoras *75*
- Salsa Verde *77*
- Tomatoes Filled with Minted Peas *98*

Mission Possible *28*

Mucous *33*

Muesli *90*

Mung Beans
- Mung Bean Salad *54*

Mushrooms
- Marvelous Marinated Mushrooms *46*
- Pasta with Mushrooms and Tomato Sauce *70*
- Zucchini Crust Pizza With Lots of Wonderful Toppings *67*

My Everything Room *120*

My Kitchen *122*

Nasal congestion *33*

Non-dairy
- Rhubarb-Apple Crisp *114*
- Slightly-Nutty-Non-Dairy-No-Egg-Pancake *90*
- Whole Oat Groat Oatmeal *92*

Non-hydrogenated cream cheese
- Lemon Cheesecake with Graham Cracker Crust *116*

Nori seaweed *37*

Nutmeg
- Cauliflower and Leek Soup *105*
- Sherried-Carrot-Butternut-Squash-Soup *108*
- Spinach with Tomatoes and Potatoes *86*
- Thick-and-Creamy-No-Cream-Celery-Soup *104*

Nutrasweet *27*

Nutritional yeast
- Corn and Avocado Salad *58*
- nutritional yeast *37*

Oat flour
- Brownies *111*
- Slightly-Nutty-Non-Dairy-No-Egg-Pancakes *90*

Oatmeal
- oatmeal *20, 31*
- Oatmeal-Raisin-Chewy-Cookies *112*
- Whole Oat Groat Oatmeal *92*

Oat milk *33*

Obesity *18, 24*

Old Appliances *114*

Olive oil
- Brown Rice with Corn and Peas *84*
- Cold, Refreshing Asparagus Salad *59*
- Crunch-Salad with-Black-Eyed Peas *52*
- Eggplant and Zucchini Bruschetta *47*
- Flat Italian Green Beans and Tomatoes with Greek Seasoning *96*
- Mango Slaw *62*
- Mung Bean Salad *54*
- Pine Nut Pesto *45*
- Red Bell Pepper Spread *46*
- Roasted Potatoes *95*
- Salsa Verde *77*
- Southwestern Corn Salad *58*
- Tomato Salsa *78*
- Traditional Tomato Bruschetta *48*
- Wheatberry Salad *57*
- Wild Rice Pilaf *53*

Omega 3 fatty acids *21, 22*

Omega 6 fatty acids *31*

One Yellow Rose *96*

Onions
- Flat Italian Green Beans and Tomatoes with Greek Seasoning *96*
- Pakoras *75*
- Peas and Macaroni *80*
- Sherried-Carrot-Butternut-Squash-Soup *108*
- Split Peas and Pasta *71*
- Tomato Salsa *78*
- Zopa de Tomate (Tomato Soup) *103*
- Zucchini Crust Pizza With Lots of Wonderful Toppings *67*

Orange juice
- A Lovely Warm Fruit Mix to End the Meal *115*
- Broccoli Ala Orange *95*
- Orange-Broccoli-Carrot-and-Raisin-Salad *51*
- orange juice *34*
- Strawberry-Mango Salad *62*

Oregano
- A-Hearty-No-Meat-Chock-Full-of-Vegetables-Good-For-You-Chili *68*
- Artichokes Italian-Style a la Connie *44*
- Barley-Corn-and-Kidney-Bean-Salad *55*
- Brown Rice with Corn and Peas *84*
- Eggplant and Zucchini Bruschetta *47*
- Italian Pasta Sauce *82*
- Marinated Green Olive Nibbles *49*
- Red Bell Pepper Spread *46*
- Roasted Potatoes *95*
- Zopa de Tomate (Tomato Soup) *103*

Organic foods *22*

Osteoporosis *20, 32, 33, 40*

P

Paprika
A-Hearty-No-Meat-Chock-Full-of-Vegetables-Good-For-You-Chili *68*
Bean and Corn Casserole *81*
Quinoa Paella without the Meat *72*

Parsley
Curried Chickpea Croquettes with Salsa Verde *76*
Nutty-Couscous-with-Mint-and-Tomatoes *83*
Roasted Potatoes *95*
Salsa Verde *77*
Split Peas and Pasta *71*
Thai Noodles, Creamy and Peanutty *74*

Pasta
Italian Pasta Sauce *82*
pasta *14, 20, 31, 32*
Pasta with Mushrooms and Tomato Sauce *70*
Split Peas and Pasta *71*

Peaches
A Lovely Warm Fruit Mix to End the Meal *115*
Slightly-Nutty-Non-Dairy-No-Egg-Pancakes *90*

Peanut butter
Thai Noodles, Creamy and Peanutty *74*

Peanuts
A Poignant Moment *69*
peanuts *83*
Thai Noodles, Creamy and Peanutty *74*

Peas
Avocado Soup, Cold and Refreshing *107*
A Word About Peas *80*
Brown Rice Medley *99*
Brown Rice with Corn and Peas *84*
Cabbage Soup *109*
peas *20, 56*
Peas and Macaroni *80*
Peas, Shoe Peg Corn and Green Bean Salad *53*
Quinoa Paella without the Meat *72*
Southwestern Corn Salad *58*
Split Peas and Pasta *71*
Tomatoes Filled with Minted Peas *98*

Pecans
Bulgur Wheat-Mint-Parsley-and-Cilantro-Salad (AKA Tabouli) *56*
Cabbage Slaw *61*
Lemon Cheesecake with Graham Cracker Crust *116*
Rhubarb-Apple Crisp *114*
Whole Oat Groat Oatmeal *92*

Pimento
A Colorful Pepper-Corn-and-Bean-Dip *45*
Corn Soup *106*
Peas, Shoe Peg Corn and Green Bean Salad *53*

Pine nuts
Cold, Refreshing Asparagus Salad *59*
Everything-But-the-Kitchen-Sink-Salad *60*
Nutty-Couscous-with-Mint-and-Tomatoes *83*
Pine Nut Pesto *45*
Ramen Noodle Slaw Mix *63*
Salsa Verde *77*

Pinto beans
A Colorful Pepper-Corn-and-Bean-Dip *45*
Bean and Corn Casserole *81*

Pitted black olives
Bean and Corn Casserole *81*

Plum
Fruit Smoothie, Delicious and Healthy *91*

Potatoes
Cabbage Soup *109*
Pakoras *75*
Roasted Potatoes *95*
Spinach with Tomatoes and Potatoes *86*

Prepared mustard
Salsa Verde *77*

Protein *19, 20, 21, 31, 32, 33, 34, 40*

Pumpernickel *31*

Pumpkin seeds
Fruit Smoothie, Delicious and Healthy *91*
Muesli *90*
pumpkin seeds *22, 25, 26, 31*

Pure maple syrup
Rhubarb-Apple Crisp *114*

Pure vanilla extract
Brownies *111*
Oatmeal-Raisin-Chewy-Cookies *112*
Rum-Raisin-Bread Pudding, Rich, and Chocolatey *119*

Q

Quinoa
Quinoa *20, 23, 31, 32*
Quinoa Paella without the Meat *72*

R

Radishes
Nutty-Couscous-with-Mint-and-Tomatoes *83*

Raisins
Bulgur Wheat-Mint-Parsley-and-Cilantro-Salad *56*
Cabbage Slaw *61*
Collard Wraps *87*
Muesli *90*
Oatmeal-Raisin-Chewy-Cookies *112*
Orange-Broccoli-Carrot-and-Raisin-Salad *51*
Rum-Raisin-Bread Pudding, Rich, and Chocolatey *119*

Raspberries
A Lovely Warm Fruit Mix to End the Meal *115*
Lemon Cheesecake with Graham Cracker Crust *116*

Red cabbage
Mango Slaw *62*

Red chilies
Pakoras *75*

Red leaf lettuce *34*

Red onion
Cabbage Slaw *61*
Crunch-Salad with-Black-Eyed Peas *52*
Southwestern Corn Salad *58*

Red pepper flakes
A-Hearty-No-Meat-Chock-Full-of-Vegetables-Good-For-You-Chili *68*
Corn and Avocado Salad *58*
Marinated Green Olive Nibbles *49*
Quinoa Paella without the Meat *72*

Red peppers
Red Bell Pepper Spread *46*

Red wine
Pasta with Mushrooms and Tomato Sauce *70*

Red wine vinegar
Brown Rice with Dill and Tomatoes *85*
Crunch-Salad with-Black-Eyed Peas *52*
Gazpacho *64*
Marinated Green Olive Nibbles *49*
Nutty-Couscous-with-Mint-and-Tomatoes *83*
Orange-Broccoli-Carrot-and-Raisin-Salad *51*
Salsa Verde *77*

Respiratory *33*

Rhubarb
Rhubarb-Apple Crisp *114*

Rice vinegar
Everything-But-the-Kitchen-Sink-Salad *60*
Thai Noodles, Creamy and Peanutty *74*

Roasted red bell peppers
Red Bell Pepper Spread *46*

Rolled oats
Muesli *90*
Rhubarb-Apple Crisp *114*

Romaine lettuce
Mango Slaw *62*

Rosemary
Red Bell Pepper Spread *46*

Rye *31*

S

Salads
Barley-Corn-and-Kidney-Bean-Salad *55*
Bulgur Wheat-Mint-Parsley-and-Cilantro-Salad (AKA Tabouli) *56*
Cabbage Slaw *61*
Cold, Refreshing Asparagus Salad *59*
Corn and Avocado Salad *58*
Crunch-Salad with-Black-Eyed Peas *52*
Everything-But-the-Kitchen-Sink-Salad *60*
Gazpacho *64*
Green-Beans-Tomatoes-and-Lots-of-Wonderful-Basil-Salad *51*
Mango Slaw *62*
Mung Bean Salad *54*
Orange-Broccoli-Carrot-and-Raisin-Salad *51*
Peas, Shoe Peg Corn and Green Bean Salad *53*
Ramen Noodle Slaw Mix *63*
Southwestern Corn Salad *58*
Strawberry-Mango Salad *62*
Tabouli Tabbouleh Taboli Tabouleh Taboule *56*
Wheatberry Salad *57*
Wild Rice Pilaf *53*

Scallions
Mung Bean Salad *54*

Sesame oil
Thai Noodles, Creamy and Peanutty *74*

Sesame seeds
Muesli *90*
sesame seeds *34*

Sherry
Sherried-Carrot-Butternut-Squash-Soup *108*

Sides
Baked Artichoke Hearts with Tomatoes & Onions *97*
Broccoli Ala Orange *95*
Brown Rice Medley *99*
Flat Italian Green Beans and Tomatoes with Greek Seasoning *96*
Roasted Potatoes *95*
Tomatoes Filled with Minted Peas *98*

Sinus infections *33*

Soups
Avocado Soup, Cold and Refreshing *107*
Cabbage Soup *109*
Cauliflower and Leek Soup *105*
Corn Soup *106*
Sherried-Carrot-Butternut-Squash-Soup *108*
Thick-and-Creamy-No-Cream-Broccoli-Soup *106*
Thick-and-Creamy-No-Cream-Celery-Soup *104*
Zopa de Tomate (Tomato Soup) *103*

Soy controversy *34*

Soy Milk *34*

Soy sauce
Brown Rice with Dill and Tomatoes *85*
Mung Bean Salad *54*
soy sauce *34*
Thai Noodles, Creamy and Peanutty *74*
Wheatberry Salad *57*

Spinach
Everything-But-the-Kitchen-Sink-Salad *60*
spinach *34*
Spinach with Tomatoes and Potatoes *86*
Split Peas and Pasta *71*
Zucchini Crust Pizza With Lots of Wonderful Toppings *67*

Splenda *27*

Standard American Diet *13, 16, 17, 18, 39, 40*

Stevia *27, 29, 30*

Stewed tomatoes
Peas and Macaroni *80*

Strawberries
Everything-But-the-Kitchen-Sink-Salad *60*
Fruit Smoothie, Delicious and Healthy *91*
Lemon Cheesecake with Graham Cracker Crust *116*
Strawberry-Mango Salad *62*

Sunflower seeds
Fruit Smoothie, Delicious and Healthy *91*
Orange-Broccoli-Carrot-and-Raisin-Salad *51*

Sunflower seed sprouts
Crunch-Salad with-Black-Eyed Peas *52*

Sweet potato
sweet potato *26, 31*
Wild Rice Pilaf *53*

Swiss chard *34*

T

Tapioca
Chia Seed Pudding *92*
Rhubarb-Apple Crisp *114*
tapioca *20*

Thyme
Red Bell Pepper Spread *46*

Tofu *20*

Tomato
A-Hearty-No-Meat-Chock-Full-of-Vegetables-Good-For-You-Chili *68*
Baked Artichoke Hearts with Tomatoes & Onions *97*
Barley-Corn-and-Kidney-Bean-Salad *55*
Brown Rice with Dill and Tomatoes *85*
Bulgur Wheat-Mint-Parsley-and-Cilantro-Salad (AKA Tabouli) *56*
Cabbage Soup *109*
Collard Wraps *87*
Corn and Avocado Salad *58*
Corn Soup *106*
Crunch-Salad with-Black-Eyed Peas *52*
Eggplant and Zucchini Bruschetta *47*
Flat Italian Green Beans and Tomatoes with Greek Seasoning *96*
Gazpacho *64*
Green-Beans-Tomatoes-and-Lots-of-Wonderful-Basil-Salad *51*
Guacamole *43*
Mango Slaw *62*
Nutty-Couscous-with-Mint-and-Tomatoes *83*
Pasta with Mushrooms and Tomato Sauce *70*
Peas and Macaroni *80*
Quinoa Paella without the Meat *72*
Spinach with Tomatoes and Potatoes *86*
Tomatoes Filled with Minted Peas *98*
Tomato Salsa *78*
Traditional Tomato Bruschetta *48*
Zopa de Tomate (Tomato Soup) *103*
Zucchini Crust Pizza With Lots of Wonderful Toppings *67*

Tomato sauce
Bean and Corn Casserole *81*
Brown Rice with Corn and Peas *84*
Flat Italian Green Beans and Tomatoes with Greek Seasoning *96*
Italian Pasta Sauce *82*
Pasta with Mushrooms and Tomato Sauce *70*

Trypsin *34*

Turmeric
Spinach with Tomatoes and Potatoes *86*

U

Uncle Chris seasoning or Greek seasoning
Flat Italian Green Beans and Tomatoes with Greek Seasoning *96*

A Valentine Treat Straight From the Heart *111*

Vegan butter
- Baked Artichoke Hearts with Tomatoes & Onions *97*
- Broccoli Ala Orange *95*
- Lemon Cheesecake with Graham Cracker Crust *116*
- Nutty-Cinnamon-Bananas *118*
- Slightly-Nutty-Non-Dairy-No-Egg-Pancakes *90*
- Tomatoes Filled with Minted Peas *98*

Vegan Mayonnaise
- Artichoke Spread *44*
- Cabbage Slaw *61*

Vegetable broth
- Cabbage Soup *109*
- Cauliflower and Leek Soup *105*
- Corn Soup *106*
- Gazpacho *64*
- Pasta with Mushrooms and Tomato Sauce *70*
- Quinoa Paella without the Meat *72*
- Sherried-Carrot-Butternut-Squash-Soup *108*
- Thick-and-Creamy-No-Cream-Broccoli-Soup *106*

Vinaigrette dressing
- Nutty-Couscous-with-Mint-and-Tomatoes *83*

Walnuts
- Brownies *111*
- Cabbage Slaw *61*
- Fruit Smoothie, Delicious and Healthy *91*
- Lemon Cheesecake with Graham Cracker Crust *116*
- Muesli *90*
- Nutty-Cinnamon-Bananas *118*
- Oatmeal-Raisin-Chewy-Cookies *112*
- Rhubarb-Apple Cris *114*
- Rum-Raisin-Bread Pudding, Rich, and Chocolatey *119*
- Tabouli Tabbouleh Taboli Tabouleh Taboule *56*
- walnuts *22, 31, 40*
- Whole Oat Groat Oatmeal *92*
- Wild Rice Pilaf *53*

What A Stove! *113*

Wheatberries
- Wheatberry Salad *57*

White cabbage
- Mango Slaw *62*

White Cannellini beans
- Bean and Corn Casserole *81*

White wine
- Thick-and-Creamy-No-Cream-Celery-Soup *104*

Whole-foods diet *27*

Whole grains *31, 32, 37*

Whole wheat flour
- Brownies *111*
- Curried Chickpea Croquettes with Salsa Verde *76*
- Oatmeal-Raisin-Chewy-Cookies *112*
- Rhubarb-Apple Crisp *114*
- Slightly-Nutty-Non-Dairy-No-Egg-Pancakes *90*
- Zucchini Crust Pizza With Lots of Wonderful Toppings *67*

Whole wheat pasta
- Split Peas and Pasta *71*
- whole wheat pasta *31*

Wild Rice
- wild rice *32*
- Wild Rice Pilaf *53*

Z

Zesty Italian Salad Dressing
- Green-Beans-Tomatoes-and-Lots-of-Wonderful-Basil-Salad *51*
- Marvelous Marinated Mushrooms *46*

Zucchini
- Eggplant and Zucchini Bruschetta *47*
- Quinoa Paella without the Meat *72*
- Traditional Tomato Bruschetta *48*
- Zucchini Crust Pizza With Lots of Wonderful Toppings *67*

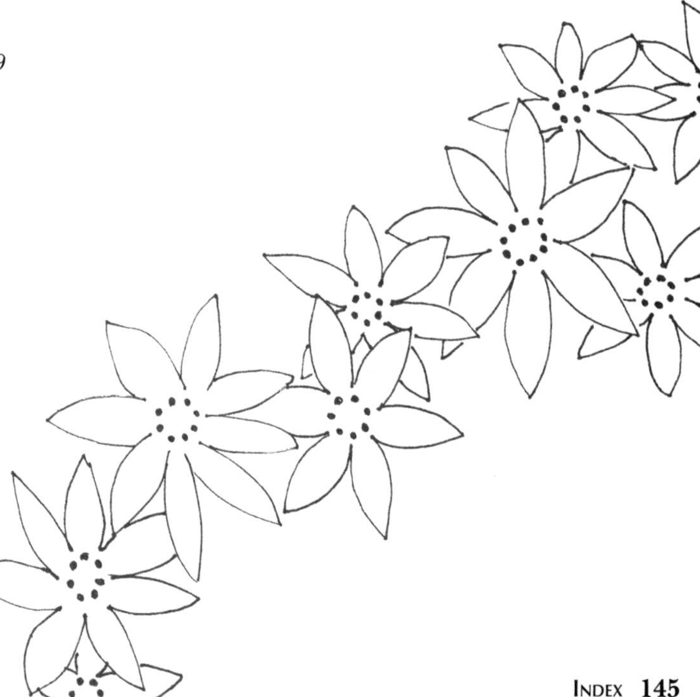

Recipe Notes

Recipe Notes

Recipe Notes